AN ILLUSTRATED HISTORY OF
COMBINE
HARVESTERS

AN ILLUSTRATED HISTORY OF
COMBINE HARVESTERS

JIM WILKIE

Ian Allan
PUBLISHING

CONTENTS

First published 2001

ISBN 0 7110 2770 6

© Jim Wilkie 2001

Published by Ian Allan Publishing

an imprint of Ian Allan Publishing Ltd, Hersham, Surrey
KT12 4RG.

Printed by Ian Allan Printing Ltd, Hersham, Surrey KT12 4RG.

Code: 0109/B

Half title page: Job done! Newly-harvested barley
pours from the discharge spout into the trailer
running alongside. The ripened crop offers the
promise of a bountiful harvest, yet this could still be
lost until the combine has actually harvested it.
    Like all combines, this New Holland TX63
devours the cut crop. Grain is separated from the
straw and husks to be stored on board, and the
remainder is discharged back on to the field to be
collected later. As seen here, the stored grain is
discharged into a trailer or other transport to be
hauled away to safe storage. This book illustrates
some of the ways this job has been tackled by
designers and farmers over the last 150 years.

Title page: An important advantage of a self-
propelled harvester is that it can cut straight into the
middle of a crop when starting. As well as
eliminating any preparation work, it means that any
particularly damp part of the field can be left to dry
out before harvesting. Here the machine is a New
Holland Clayson 8055. The rotary air cleaner for
the radiator is visible to the left of the model
identification.

Front cover: A Claas high-output combine making
short work of a field of oil seed rape. The driver is
comfortably seated in his air conditioned cab.
Peter Adams

Back cover upper: Steam threshing looks old-
fashioned, yet only eighty years ago, this represented
the latest technology in post-harvest processing.

Back cover lower: While they both carry the
Massey Ferguson name, there is a huge difference
in comfort and output between these two combines
separated by over 30 years of development.
Peter Adams

ACKNOWLEDGEMENTS

My thanks to the many operators, owners and farmers who answered questions about their machines; many of the most interesting conversations took place long before this book was planned.

Most of the photographs of dismantled combines were taken at Midland Combines at Long Bennington near Newark, Nottinghamshire (Tel 01400 281506); they are well worth a ring if you need second-hand parts, or sieves and augers reconditioned. These were supplemented by combines awaiting customers at George Coles Tractors of Dorset.

Most of all, thanks to the farmers around the world who are growing grain crops — without them there would be no need for combines but we would all starve!

PICTURE CREDITS
All the pictures reproduced in this book have been supplied from the author's collection unless credited otherwise.

FINDING OUT MORE

Most combine collectors and restorers are likely to be members of the National Vintage Tractor and Engine Club or one of the more-locally based collectors' societies. Certain vintage events in the autumn feature a working area where combines may be seen at work. Such events are likely to be advertised in Tourist Offices, local papers and in the vintage machinery press.

The Author welcomes your comments, questions and feedback, either through the Publishers, or by email to Weylode@aol.com

SAFETY WARNING

- The machinery used in harvesting on farms is big and heavy and powerful. Be warned — it can inflict serious injury. By the nature of its design it has blind spots — the driver may not see you before you get injured.
- Keep away from parked machinery! Even when it is at rest you risk injury by falling from machinery or machinery falling on you.
- Grain stores are dangerous places, and every year people are tragically killed by piles of grain.
- Keep out of fields and buildings for your own safety.
- Farmers are very busy people especially at harvest time, and every year even experienced farmers and farm workers suffer the injuries described above. Without experience you run an even greater risk of injury.

The photographs in this book were taken with the knowledge of the operators who were fully aware of the photographer's presence.

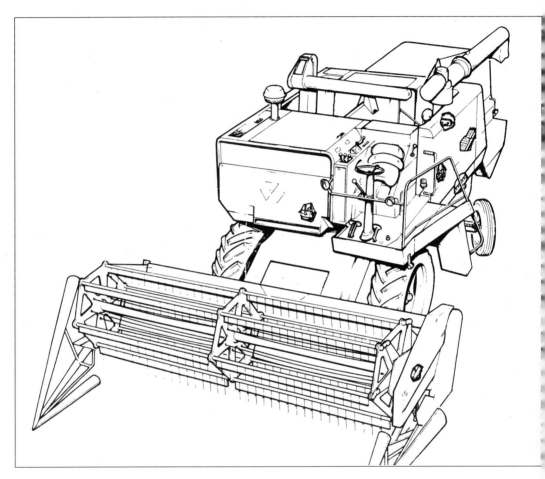

A line drawing of the front nearside elevation of a Massey Ferguson 400 series combine.

INTRODUCTION:
19TH-CENTURY ANCESTORS

The growing of wheat, oats and barley in particular is a very efficient way of turning the assets of soil, rain and sunshine into food. Grain is relatively easy to store. It is a concentrated source of nutrition, which makes it easier to transport. Both humans and livestock can make use of it. Without grain we would starve.

A combine harvester is a specialised machine to harvest grain. It appears to be one of the most complicated machines to be found on most farms and is probably the most expensive machine owned and operated by most farmers, yet it does a job that anybody could do with their bare hands.

Enter a field of ripened grain, bend down and snap off an individual stalk just above the ground. Place the head between the hands and rub them vigorously in a circular motion. With luck in one hand will be a length of straw, a number of grains, and some loose husk.

Bend over and blow gently on your hand. Correctly judged, loose and fluffy material will blow away, leaving the grain. Discard the straw on the ground and place the grain into a storage receptacle.

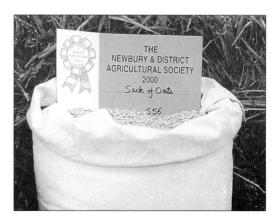

Top: A good sample of feed wheat. Grown for its high yields, this would be milled and incorporated into animal feed. The combine designer's job is to build a machine to harvest as much as possible from the growing crop with as little damage to the grain as possible. A good-quality sample should have well-filled grains for the highest feeding value. Apart from treatment during growing, quality will be affected by the decision when to harvest.

Middle: Much the same applies to feeding barley, but with one extra problem. Each grain of barley has an awn or sharp spike attached to it. In a good sample these should all have been removed while passing through the combine.

Bottom: Oats are less commonly grown, but they will grow in areas where wheat and barley would not yield well.

All three samples shown here are very clean with no sign of foreign matter such as green trash. Weed-control sprays have reduced this problem, and careful setting of the combine should eliminate most of it. For a competition like this the grain would probably have been cleaned again afterwards. Any of these samples would convince a combine driver that his machine was correctly adjusted.

Rubbing a head of wheat between the hands leaves a mixture of chaff and grain.

A gentle breath will blow away the light chaff. With correct judgement, nearly all the grain is left and most chaff blown away.

Congratulations! You have just witnessed the hand-harvesting of a stalk of straw.

At its simplest that's all a combine harvester does. However, in a field there are literally millions of other stalks needing the same treatment! Is it any wonder that farmers over the years have been seeking better ways of doing this job? Farmers are only prepared to pay so much to buy a combine harvester because it does the job a lot more efficiently, a lot more quickly and a lot more cheaply than employing hundreds of people on boring, monotonous low-paid work.

Oddly enough, most people who work on the land still start their harvest by hand as described above. It offers a quick method of assessing whether the grain is fit to harvest. Until the crop is ready, rubbing out grains will be much more difficult. Trying to bite a grain to assess whether it is still milky or has

hardened enough to be fit for harvesting can confirm the judgement.

The combine harvester has released hundreds of thousands of people from boring and monotonous work harvesting crops. Many have moved to live in towns confident that farmers will continue to produce enough food to prevent them from ever going hungry. Only in the second half of the 20th century did hunger become unusual in Britain. Much of this is due to the efforts of farmers both in Britain and abroad producing food more and more cheaply. Savings made on food have left more income available to spend on other things like motor cars, better houses, entertainment and holidays. Nobody spends money on comfort or pleasure while they are hungry. Worryingly, if you study the world reserves of grain the situation is far more perilous than most people realise.

The combine is only the latest in a long line of machines intended to mechanise different stages of harvesting cereal crops, yet the extraordinary thing is that an agricultural engineer familiar with machinery produced a hundred years ago would easily understand the main working principles of a combine harvester produced today. This may seem pretty surprising, but let's have a look at the various main components of a combine, which have all evolved from various ancestor machines.

THE SCYTHE

When harvesting cereal crops by hand the traditional method was to cut the grain with a scythe, but even that was an improvement on the simple sharpened hook that had previously been used. With a scythe, the harvester could stand almost upright while cutting the crop. Behind him his helper would be stooping and tying the crop into bundles called sheaves. In turn, six or eight sheaves would be made into stooks to dry.

To make a stook, two parallel rows of sheaves were stood up but leaning over with their tops touching. If built properly this made a stable structure capable of

shedding some rain but exposed to drying winds. By this method harvesting could start well before the crop was fit, and the ripening process was completed in the stooks while the crop was drying.

A cradle on a scythe made it more cumbersome but helped to leave the cut crop in bunches. Even so, making sheaves was still hard work, and plenty of willing labour was needed. In the new territories of the United States and Canada there was plenty of land suitable for growing cereal crops, but there was certainly not enough labour to cope with the job of harvesting.

The spread of the railways meant that more grain could be sold at acceptable prices if it could be harvested, so there was considerable demand for any machine that offered the prospect of speeding this job, whereby the same number of people could harvest a bigger area.

THE REAPER

It was the prestige of the 1851 Great Exhibition that attracted the McCormick reaper to the British market. This was the first machine to speed the harvesting of cereal crops. Already widely used in the

The secret of scything was getting into a slow unhurried rhythm and keeping the blade sharp. The best cutting action was sliding the blade along the stem rather than trying to chop through it. Any attempt to rush the scythe involved large amounts of almost unproductive effort. In a group of mowers, the largest area was always covered by an old boy who looked as if he wasn't even trying for high output.

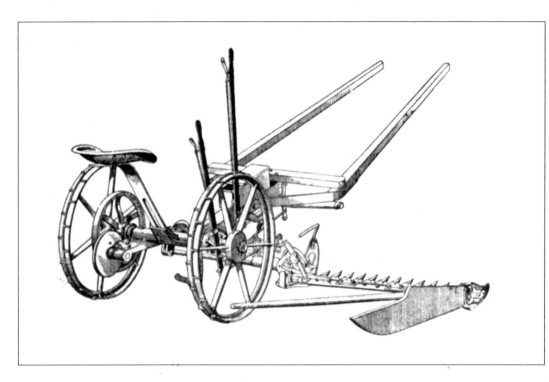

Above: A mower cuts with a scissoring action. On this early version only one wheel drives a bevel wheel, which in turn makes the mower blade travel backwards and forwards to do the cutting. Here for the first time was a horse-drawn implement to replace the scythe. The seat enabled the rider's weight to give more grip, and to a horseman used to stumbling along behind an implement all day it was a most welcome innovation.

Below: By today's standards the Deering sail reaper was a simple and uncomplicated machine. In use, it drastically reduced the amount of hand-scything needed to harvest a crop. The cut crop fell on to the table, where it was swept off by the revolving sails in bunches ready to be tied into sheaves. This newly restored example was exhibited by its owner at the Great Dorset Steam Fair.

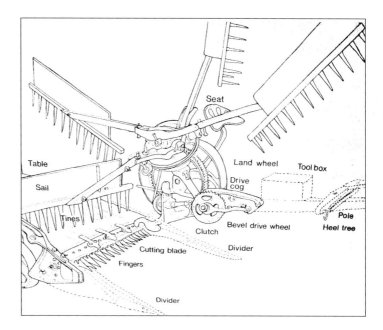

Seat
Table
Sail
Tines
Land wheel
Tool box
Drive cog
Pole
Heel tree
Bevel drive wheel
Clutch
Divider
Cutting blade
Fingers
Divider

Below right: How the reaper moved through the crop.

United States, this two-horse machine cut the straw and allowed it to fall back on to a table. From there it was raked off in bundles by a second operator carried on the machine.

The Royal Agricultural Society arranged practical trials of the machine in Essex. Also on show and on trial was a similar machine from Obed Hussey, but it was judged that the McCormick machine was the more successful, while Hussey's more closely resembled a grass mower. The stubble length was about 8 inches and, with two horses, the machine was cutting 1½ acres per hour, which compared with about 1 acre being a good day's work for one man with a scythe. Even if the horses could manage only 6 hours of useful work, this was progress: a horseman and his helper could achieve four times as much as swinging a scythe. The raked-off bundles still had to be tied into sheaves by assistants, but horsepower and machinery was assisting with cutting the crop for the first time.

In a later development the man with the rake was replaced with an automatic raking apparatus driven, like the cutter bar, by the mower wheels. The replaced man could now be tying sheaves instead; this was still done using some of the cut straw platted by hand into a band.

THE REAPER BINDER

By 1876 McCormick was able to offer a reaper binder device that cut the crop, raked it automatically

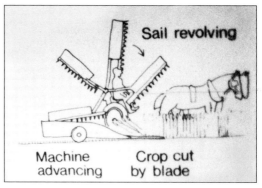

Sail revolving

Machine advancing   Crop cut by blade

and tied it into bundles using wire. To attract examples of these machines to Britain, the Royal Agricultural Society put up a substantial Gold Medal award. The contest attracted eight self-tying machines, including three American machines using wire. In 1877 the judges felt that they needed more information, and by 1878 they had awarded the Gold Medal to the McCormick machine, with Wood highly commended.

Binders made use of several mechanisms that would later prove advantageous. To cut the crop a long knife with triangular blades was pulled and pushed backwards and forwards through guides, giving a scissoring action that severed the stalks, which then fell back on to wide canvas belts running over rollers. While one belt transported the stalks sideways, two belts were needed to transport them up

11

Above: Few farmers were interested in machinery, and a line drawing like this was often their first information on a new innovation. This self-tying binder, shown in the working position, must have seemed an unimaginably complicated machine at first — a good farmer was judged by his ability with livestock, not machinery.

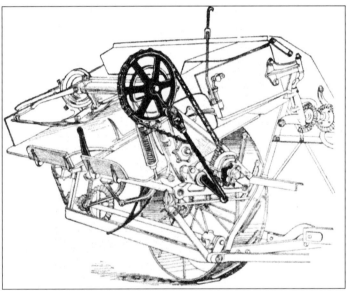

Left: To add to his worries was this close-up of the various components that packed and shaped a sheaf before tying it and discharging it.

and over the binder drive wheel. This transport method was gentle and required comparatively little power.

The wire used for binding was, however, not totally satisfactory, as animals could suffer serious internal injury if they swallowed a piece; with macabre humour this was known as 'hardware disease'. Could it be replaced with something better? Sisal twine proved to be the answer, and a special knotter was developed to tie the sheaves. This ingenious mechanism gripped the cut end of a length of sisal twine and, when a curved needle passed over the top

of a bunch of straw, the knotter grabbed the twine gripped in the needle and in one movement knotted the two bits of string. Before cutting the knot from the twine it also grabbed the twine to be cut. When the knotter was working well the result was each sheaf neatly knotted with no delays. The original inspiration was supposed to have come from watching a dog playing with its lead.

The knotter led to the introduction of the reaper binder. Now a machine could do the whole job, leaving tied sheaves lying on the ground. The high output of these machines meant that everybody who

The Hermaphrodite wagon consisted of a conventional two-wheeled cart, which, with the addition of a fore-carriage, could be converted into a four-wheeled wagon. At harvest time this increased the load of sheaves it could carry.

had previously been employed in raking or tying sheaves could concentrate on getting them into stooks to aid the drying process.

The arrival of binder twine marked another first — to tie sheaves a farmer now had to buy in a consumable product. In turn, sisal became a useful cash crop for growers in Mexico and East Africa. Most binder manufacturers had their own twine production plants, providing another profitable trade for dealers. Used binder twine was ideal for tying sacks and for many repair jobs around the farm.

A familiar pattern was emerging. Every time a new machine was introduced, fewer people were needed to do the job, yet more hard work was created by jobs the machine did not do.

By the beginning of the 20th century most progressive farmers used a binder. After drying, sheaves could be carted in and stacked for long-term storage (if they were stacked too wet, it would cause the stack to heat, spoiling the contents). However, once safely stacked, losses could still occur.

RATS AND MICE

Fields of growing grain have always provided an ideal environment for mice, but where do they go in winter? Straw stacks provided a welcoming home; with plenty of food and shelter, nests could easily be constructed away from the worst weather. The trouble was that the mice were competing for the grain with the farmer, who hoped to thresh it out of the stack later. Rats also found that a straw stack suited their requirements for winter accommodation.

Some cunning ideas were used to reduce these losses. Today, newcomers to the country often like to decorate their front lawns with staddle stones, which, as far as they are concerned, are just quaintly shaped stones found on farms. However, their original function was to support a granary or even individual stacks off the ground. The idea was to make it far more difficult for rats and mice to get at the stored grain.

This was fine in theory but was often frustrated by human nature. With the granary up in the air, a convenient dry area was left underneath, and the temptation was always to use it to store hand tools or loose equipment. Unfortunately, as rodents are good acrobats, this was a bit like installing a ladder. In practice, few farms could build all their stacks up in the air on staddle stones. More typically the base of

Now sold as country ornaments, staddle stones once performed an important job. Used to support a granary, the tapered profile with the mushroom cap provided support yet made it impossible for rats and mice to climb up and enter the store.

the stack would be branches of wood covered with old straw; this kept the stacks off the ground, preventing moisture soaking up, but offered no obstacle to rats or mice. Unless stored inside a barn, the sheaves could suffer weather damage, and outdoor stacks needed the protection of thatching. Ultimately, only the arrival of the combine would eliminate these particular causes of loss.

A farm dog and cats would help keep the rodent population down, but the only really effective method of pest control within a stack was to thresh it and bag off the grain. With the use of a binder a farmer and his men could cut and stack a bigger area of cereals, but there was little value in a stack of sheaves. What was needed was the separation of the saleable grain, while the straw could be used on the farm.

For many years this had been achieved with the aid of a flail. With considerable effort this hand tool could be used to beat the grain from the straw. It was rather faster than hand rubbing, but it was a tiring and monotonous job. However, it did provide winter

work for many farm labourers, the same men who would previously have been needed for mowing and tying sheaves.

As you might imagine, these labourers were very concerned to hear rumours of new machinery that could do the work of a flail. The introduction of early machines was the signal for local riots, with masked intruders smashing up the machines to protect the jobs of labourers who would otherwise be out of work. Despite this, by the start of the 20th century most progressive farmers had their sheaves threshed by some form of threshing machine, and the flail was becoming less common. Together with a reaper binder, the harvest was beginning to be mechanised.

THE THRESHING MACHINE

The threshing machine was by far the most elaborate and sophisticated machine seen on most farms. It also needed considerable power to operate it, and this could be obtained either from some form of horse-driven device or more often a steam engine. Few farmers could face the mechanical complications of owning and operating a threshing machine and steam engine, so travelling threshing contractors did much of the work.

The early threshing machine was a substantial wooden-framed box with plenty of pulleys and belts visible on the outside. It was presided over by a representative of the threshing contractor, who seemed to make the most unreasonable demands on the people feeding the sheaves into his machine or taking away the threshed grain, the straw and the waste products.

Internally the actions of a threshing machine were very similar to those of today's combine. The drive belt normally drove a pulley on one end of the actual threshing drum. This drum separated the straw and grain; fitted with a number of serrated bars, it rotated inside a concave. The clearance between the individual bars on the drum and the bars on the wall of the concave could be accurately adjusted, so any heads of grain caught in the gap were vigorously rubbed, in an action very like rubbing your hands to separate the grain from the straw head.

Set correctly, the drum would separate the grain from the straw. Most grain fell through the chamber and on to the various riddles or sieves. Depending on the manufacturer, these would be made of either perforated metal or drilled wood.

There were several layers of sieves, so oversize material such as complete seed heads would be held back by the first sieves, and returned to the threshing drum to go through the rubbing process again. Satisfactory grain would be directed through another sieve, while only undersize grain would pass through the third sieve. Good grain flowed towards a part of the threshing machine where it could be bagged off.

However, mixed with this grain was a lot of lighter material generally known as chaff or cavings. The sieves were not suitable to separate this from the grain, so a substantial fan was mounted in the base of the threshing machine, and a blast of air from this fan was directed over the sieves at a point where the grain would be falling, the aim being to blow the light rubbish away from the grain.

This air blast was not a new idea. Grain that had been separated with a flail also contained much rubbish, and harvest barns were usually designed to be draughty! With both doors of the barn open, the prevailing wind could pass through. By dropping the grain from a height, this wind would tend to separate the light material from the heavier grain, and on a windy day this exercise would be repeated until the light material had all been blown out of the grain. This operation was known as winnowing.

The fan on a threshing machine produced a more predictable 'wind', which could be directed where it was most useful. Too strong a wind could blow good grain out of a threshing machine to waste. As we will discover, even a hundred years later combine operators still adjust air blasts to ensure a clean sample without waste.

Some loose grain remained trapped in the straw and would go to waste. To prevent this, straw walkers gave the straw a vigorous shaking, the trapped grains falling clear on to the top sieve while the straw passed out of the threshing machine.

If you see a threshing machine at work, the overpowering impression is one of noise and vibration. Running empty, the drum should rotate smoothly with just a characteristic hum caused by the movement of the air as it spins, while the power unit driving it will be making its own characteristic chuffing noise. Most of the noise will come from the various reciprocating parts of the threshing machine: the sieves will be swinging backwards and forwards, and the straw walkers will be rising up and down in response to the rotation of the crankshaft. The fan will also be making a characteristic noise blowing large quantities of air through the machine.

But if you think that sounds noisy, wait till the threshing itself starts! The man on the threshing machine is responsible for feeding each sheaf into the machine evenly, aiming for a uniform pace to achieve the best possible threshing. Even so, the threshing drum produces a characteristic deep hum or groan as each sheaf enters it. At the same time the load increases on the steam engine driving it, and the gentle chuffing becomes a much sharper bark as the engine starts to work harder. As the straw passes through the machine clouds of dust will begin to emerge from the air blasts, and some arrangement will be needed to dispose of the straw. A typical English threshing machine could keep 10 to 14 men working hard ministering to its needs.

By the start of the 20th century the flail was used mainly by smallholders, although larger farmers might assess how a crop might later thresh out by trying the odd sheaf with a flail. Most progressive farmers had their sheaves threshed by some form of threshing machine, which in a few days could complete what would be a whole winter's work with flails. Already more labourers were taking jobs in towns and leaving the land.

However, as already mentioned, few farmers would want to face owning and operating so elaborate and sophisticated a machine and its attendant steam engine, and while their reasons might vary they made good sense.

Left: This traveller's model was used by Edward Humphries to explain the workings of his design of threshing machine. Taking it packed in its protective case, a representative, probably Mr Humphries himself, would perhaps travel by train to attend upon a prospective customer, who would be able to study the details of its design and operation. Most of the design was orthodox, although the open bucket conveyor was rather unusual.

Below: A cut-away view of a Foster threshing machine. Straw enters the drum (A) in the concave (B) from above, then travels along the straw shakers (C) and out at the opening marked 'Straw'. Most of the grain is rubbed out through the concave, falling on to the flat boards (D) that direct the flow of material to a perforated board (1 — the cavings riddle) where it can drop through. Preventing any light material falling through is the fan (F), the air blast from which is blowing up through the same holes, blowing any light material out through the exit marked 'Cavings'. As the grain travels back along the bottom shoe (E), dust can still drop through, so some of the air blast swirls the dust round and out at the exit marked 'Dust'. The grain then drops on to riddle 2, and again wind from the fan lifts off any light rubbish, which is also blown out at G. Oversize rubbish like seed heads comes out as 'Capes' together with more dust. (Dealing with this build-up with the fan swirling it round is a thoroughly unpleasant job.) Acceptable grain passes to H, which is a spout discharging into the base of the elevator. At the top of its journey the grain enters a rotary awner and smutter (K), which removes barley awns before passing over two more sieves, 6 and 7. Again an air blast from a second fan (M) blows off trash and rubbish. Undersized, thin and damaged grain leaves by spout P to be sacked off as poultry feed. The rotary screen (N) is the last test, which sorts the grains into correct and undersize. Saleable grain runs out of the sacking-off spouts at 'Finished grain'. Notice how easily a feeder could fall into the drum and suffer injuries. Most British threshers followed this layout. With their riddles and shoes being agitated back and forth, a threshing machine at full output was noisy, dusty and impressive.

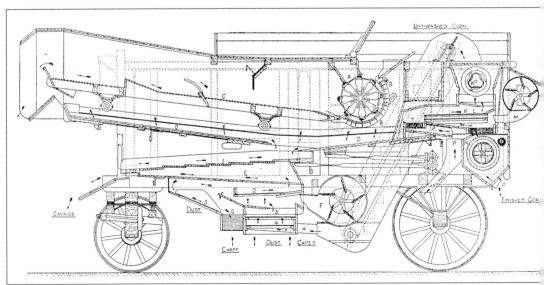

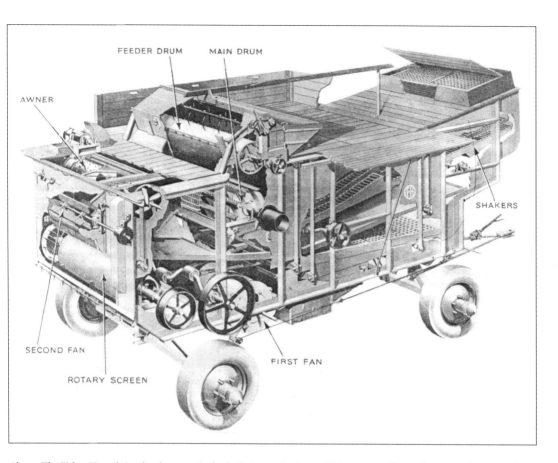

FEEDER DRUM   MAIN DRUM

AWNER

SHAKERS

SECOND FAN

FIRST FAN

ROTARY SCREEN

Above: The Fisher Humphries thresher was similar in design to the Foster. This cut-away illustration is seen from the other side. One significant difference is the extra feeder drum, which, as well as promoting a more even flow of material into the drum, reduces the risk of injury to the operator from the drum itself.

Right: Straw being discharged from a Foster threshing drum after a thorough shaking by the straw walkers to ensure all impurities and grain have been shaken out. Lower down in the machine, impurities, broken straw and rubbish from the sieves are also being fed on to the same elevator. Both will be carried up into the air where the small matter will prove a nuisance as it blows into the faces of the stackers. This machine is operating at the Much Marcle Steam Rally, Herefordshire, in 2000.

Above: Carter's of Billingshurst manufactured the 'Unique' elevator. As shown here it could take the output of a threshing drum and lift and discharge it into the ideal position to build a stack. Power would come either from a belt from the threshing machine or, as in this case, from an engine mounted within the frame. The height of the discharge was adjusted by using winches to tighten or slacken the two support cables. On many farms an elevator was the first mechanical handling equipment acquired.

Left: Where the money comes out! The arrangements for bagging-off grain from the Foster threshing drum. Under the lift-up flap a rotary screen is mounted across the back. As this revolves it allows the escape of any thin and shrivelled grain, ensuring that the remaining grain flowing into the sacks is of good quality. The nearest sack carries the markings of United Sack Contractors, formed by the merger of various sack-hirers.

The first power source for driving a threshing machine was the portable steam engine such as this one, seen at Much Marcle Steam Rally, Herefordshire, in 2000. Although it could generate power to drive other machinery, it still needed to be transported from job to job pulled by one or more horses.

Left: This daunting notice helped to ensure that only the contractor's men got on to the threshing drum.

Below: A typical small barn or Scotch thresher. Its small size and modest output suited frequent use for small amounts of threshing on one farm. It is seen out in the open at the Great Dorset Steam Fair.

Trussing was the first mechanical method of dealing with straw from the threshing machine. Its action was based on the binder but with two knotters. The resulting trusses were light enough to be handled and stacked like sheaves.

Compared with other farm machinery a threshing machine was expensive to purchase, and a skilled man was needed to supervise its satisfactory operation. Much the same applied to its power unit. Fifty years later much the same comments were made about combines on farms. Travelling threshing contractors therefore took on much of the work. A big gang was needed to thresh at maximum output, and running a threshing machine disrupted the normal routine of all but the biggest farm.

In Scotland a rather different and smaller design of threshing machine became popular on many farms, which dated back to development work by Andrew Meikle in the late 18th century. Instead of needing a large crew to operate it, the smaller Scottish machine could be operated by two or three men, providing steady winter work for a few men over a much longer period. The threshing drum was much smaller and carried a large number of protruding pegs, as did the concave. The threshing action came from the pegs passing between one another and forcing the grain to separate. The straw produced was much more battered than from an English machine, but on a mixed farm this was not important, as typically the straw would be used within a few days of threshing.

The Government has always taken a close interest in grain production; if nothing else, statistics could give an early warning of impending shortages. Officers of Customs & Excise, acting as Corn Inspectors, were responsible for compiling statistics. This letterbox is still in place in Stow-on-the-Wold in Gloucestershire, and meant that returns could be made even when the office was closed.

Would the development of new machinery and the opening up of the new lands of the United States and Canada be enough to keep the world fed? In 1898 Sir William Crookes, President of the British Association for the Advancement of Science, was pessimistic. He warned his audience to expect world wheat shortages by 1930, but happily the scientific research he was trying to encourage meant that his date was wrong.

By 1900 increased overseas production had started to affect corn prices in Britain — imported grain could undercut home-grown supplies, despite the cost of shipping and rail freight to move it to the ports. These falling prices meant that British farmers were more inclined to reduce the amount of wheat grown rather than invest in even more machinery.

With the binder and the threshing machine, most of the components needed to make a combine harvester by now existed somewhere on the world's farms, but all of them would need some more development before a major change could be expected on the harvest scene.

1. Increased Mechanisation, 1900-20

By the end of the 19th century machines were available to do some of the hard work. The only problem was that few farmers were engineers. Excellent judges of horseflesh, yes; good at planning work to keep a large number of men employed; and skilled in judging just the right moment for cultivation. But engineering? No, thank you.

As we have seen, for most farmers a threshing contractor was the answer. Here was a man able to say, 'I will bring the necessary machinery to thresh out the grain from your stack of sheaves. The grain will be put into the sacks you provide. The threshed straw will be left nearby in a heap or stack for you to use. The weed seeds and reject grain will be left in separate piles for you to feed to hens or pigs. All you have to do is provide coal and water for my steam engine and pay me so much a day or so much a ton threshed.

'I will be responsible for keeping the machinery, running including all repairs and servicing needed. I will provide as many skilled men as you want to pay for, but I can make up the gang with men you or your neighbours can provide.'

Put like this, a threshing contractor was the answer to most farmers' problems. The offer certainly sounded attractive.

The Cakewalk has always been a popular fairground attraction, and riders can experience some idea of how straw is moved along a straw walker in a threshing machine. In both cases cranks impart a lift and forward/lower and backward motion. Without the grab rails, riders would soon be off the far end!

A threshing contractor was an excellent operator of machinery. How did he get started? Every contractor's family will have a different story, but certain features are so common that we can produce an almost typical history.

As a youngster he would have been drawn to machinery of any type, and from this he would have earned a reputation of being 'good with machinery'. So who was this wonderful chap? Backgrounds varied, but common qualities were a willingness to work hard for a modest reward, a skill at operating a steam engine, and sufficient mechanical knowledge to appreciate the importance of the proper maintenance of quite sophisticated equipment.

While these qualities could be found in many skilled working men, three other qualities set the contractor apart:

1. A good character was vital in attracting the necessary backing to take that first step into contracting, and a good reputation in the district was valuable. You might think these two are the same, but they are not quite. Country folk have long memories; even selfish actions recalled from school, or as a child, could deter certain customers from using a particular contractor.

The winnower used a large fan and a selection of riddles to improve the quality of grain by removing light rubbish and sieving it to a specified size. Winnower design remained unchanged for many years and very similar features could be found in most combine designs.

2. At some time the contractor would get a 'lucky break'. Maybe he was allowed to restore a neglected and disused machine belonging to a neighbour. Maybe his employer wanted to retire or sell up. Maybe with an old or worn-out machine he was able to make a start. The next big step came when a machinery dealer, manufacturer or even a banker identified him as worth backing. For a potentially good customer they could construct some special deal that would make it possible to update the equipment and offer a better service.

3. Most contractors were teetotallers or had only a modest thirst. They needed to be discreet about their customers' business. No farmer would be happy if his contractor was known to be talking of his yields as disappointing, or stacks as badly made. Long before the general use of the telephone or radio, indiscreet remarks in a local pub would soon spread.

The business end of a Clayton & Shuttleworth thresher. Drive was applied by a long belt to the small-diameter pulley on the left, and grain was bagged off through the four outlets at the rear. The all-timber construction made such a drum very vulnerable to fire. The working platform is still folded in the travelling position. Clayton & Shuttleworth was a noted steam engine builder that expired in the late 1920s, soon after launching a massive trailed combine.

While we associate the Foden name with lorries, this Cheshire firm used to manufacture threshing drums for use with its steam engines. The body is diagonally planked for additional strength, and restoration has involved making new sides for the working platform.

A good contractor would pick up more customers. Then a second outfit could be justified and expansion started. To complement threshing, haulage contracts and timber-sawing work might be taken on to keep both men and machines at profitable work throughout the year. With luck, skilled and enthusiastic sons would be growing up to run these activities, and daughters could well bring in sons-in-law to complement the operation. Much of their low wages would be returned to mother as board and lodging, and effectively this kept the money in the family.

The founder might stick to threshing and become cautious, while younger members of the family would argue passionately that the future lay in change. Later these would be the sort of businesses that would be ideally equipped to become the first operators of combines. Change could be a tractor rather than steam, combines rather than threshing, motor lorries rather than steam haulage. This could lead either to a change in direction for the business or some members

leaving and striking out on their own. If the decision was taken to add combining to their services, a background in threshing was a great help.

A farmer's opinions of a threshing contractor could vary widely. Certainly they solved the problem of getting the crop threshed. However, using one was not always the ideal answer. Early contractors used a portable steam engine, which had to be moved by a team of horses from job to job. Since the farmer had to provide the horses, that meant one or two more days' work lost moving the machinery on to and away from the farm.

The farmer was also expected to provide the coal to run the steam engine. Coal could be bought relatively cheaply, delivered to the nearest railway station. To save cost most farmers would order either a cartload or more usually a railway truckload and cart it back to the farm with their own cart. As the farmer was supplying the fuel, there was little incentive for the contractor to worry about fuel economy, and most favoured the less efficient 'simple' steam engine despite its greater appetite for coal.

You can still see this at a steam rally. Most of the steam engines described as originally belonging to threshing contractors are unsophisticated single-cylinder 'simple' engines. The bark of their exhaust when working hard is made by steam going to waste from the blast-pipe up the chimney. By contrast, a 'compound' engine, which uses the steam twice, first in a high-pressure then in a low-pressure cylinder, extracts more energy from it, saving fuel and producing a softer engine note when working hard.

The normal practice with a self-propelled traction engine was that it would leave a job with the coal bunker filled to give enough fuel to get to the next job. Even today a similar arrangement is adopted at most steam rallies: exhibitors arrive with fairly empty bunkers and leave with them filled.

Quality of coal has always been a sore point with engine owners. Good Welsh steam coal was highly prized, but being dearer than others, many farmers would try and fob off the driver with poorer grades. This produced more ash and clinker, making the driver's job more difficult and reducing the power available. For export markets, where coal was expensive, most traction engine builders could offer the option of a firebox that would burn threshed straw or wood.

Water is not a fuel, but a steam engine still requires large quantities to keep going. Unless the steamer was positioned alongside a stream or pond that was clean enough to use, a water cart would be required. With a capacity of around 100-200 gallons, the water had to be pumped in by hand or lifted in using a bucket. Then a horse had to pull the load, usually uphill, to where the engine was working.

A rickyard full of straw stacks was a worrying place to site a steam engine, which could give off sparks and start a fire. Other fire risks arose from a discarded smoking material such as a cigarette end or from a bearing running hot. Farmers were advised to keep buckets of water and wet sacks to hand in case of fire.

In the United States manufacturers of threshing machines, or separators as they were called, favoured the peg-type drum. In grain-growing areas labour was so short that hired hands were far better paid than English labourers of the time. As a result, farmers were willing to pay more if output could be increased without needing more labour. Manufacturers responded with labour-saving devices, their aim being always to reduce the number of workers needed to run a machine.

Although straw was of no use on those farms without livestock, customers who required it to be stacked could specify devices that would convey the straw into a stack away from the threshing area. These devices could swing over in an arc to reduce the stackers' work, and the discharge could be set manually or, on more expensive designs, mechanically. The actual conveying could be by wind from a belt-driven fan or by a positive chain conveyor.

Other devices blew away the cavings and light waste, and mechanical devices were fitted to assist with automatic self-feeding. Typically a conveyor would carry sheaves up to the feeder, and governors would slow the feeding rate to prevent jams if the machine was losing speed or the feeders were overloading the machine. A hundred years later designers were working on devices for combines that did much the same. Fitting a weigher to the delivery spout meant that weighed grain could flow loose straight into a cart. This eliminated the job of changing sacks and check-weighing each one. With

American 'separators' were designed to save labour. The pipe on the left labelled 'straw chute' was swung round to blow the threshed straw into a pile with the minimum of effort. At the front (right-hand) end, the 'sheaf carrier' folded out to make a horizontal trough into which sheaves could be pitched head first. They were conveyed into the band cutter where the string was cut, allowing the straw to feed into the drum.

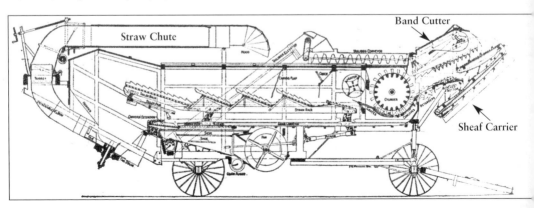

26

these aids it was possible to run such a separator with a far smaller crew.

It also made it practical to set up a separator actually in the harvest field. Sheaves could then be carted direct from the stook to the separator. This eliminated the considerable jobs of stacking, protecting and pitching the sheaves later in the year. Climate differences meant that sheaves could remain in the field far longer than would be prudent in Britain. Only the grain was retained, with the straw being discarded often without stacking.

A few farmers took these developments even further. Could they eliminate the binder and stooks? Could the standing crop be cut and fed straight into the separator? Could the separator be towed around the field to make this possible? Would this save labour?

Inventive farmers and engineers started experimenting. They dragged a separator along the field, feeding newly cut straw straight into it. Results were promising. The most urgent need for such a machine was in California where it was possible to grow large areas of grain at very profitable prices. However, competition from other employers was making it impossible to get sufficient labour to harvest with sheaves.

The first attempts to produce a driven machine used power obtained from a land-wheel drive, which needed massive teams of mules to drag the machine along, most of the effort being required to generate the necessary power to carry out the threshing. Only a few of these machines were built, although they did work on the large-scale farms of California.

Owners were soon reminded of the problems of putting together and controlling big mule teams of 40 or more, and were keen to try any other sources of power. The first alternative was the use of massive steam engines to haul land-wheel-drive combines; after the harvest they could be used to haul ploughs. Two early firms in this business of making combines and tractors were Holt and Best, which would later merge to form the Caterpillar Tractor Company. It was the need for powerful tractors that would not sink in soft ground that encouraged the development

The International Titan was the first tractor produced in quantity that was recognised to have the power to drive a full-sized threshing machine. Although they were rather light to tow or manoeuvre a drum under difficult conditions, they were used by the Army to help with threshing and the baling of forage. The Foster threshing machine is still presented by Rupert Cove who first threshed commercially with it over 60 years ago.

of tracklaying tractors. Almost a century later Caterpillar offers combines on tracks for the same reasons.

Later, mounting a petrol engine on the combine to drive the threshing machinery removed the need for wheel drive and meant less power was needed to pull a combine.

At first it was believed that huge combine harvesters could only be useful in the hot areas of California where the grain could be cut completely ripe. However, other major wheat growers in areas in the Midwest of the United States, Australia and South America were keenly interested in the possibilities.

Britain, however, had more pressing problems than harvesting large areas of crops. Until the outbreak of World War 1 in 1914 cereal growing had not been particularly profitable, and the acreage grown had declined. Despite the Royal Navy, German submarines sank many ships bringing in imported grain, and suddenly politicians realised that home-grown grain was the answer. Prices rose, and plenty of praise was heaped on farmers. To aid this process, War Agricultural Executive Committees were set up to encourage production. Even the Army was used to relieve labour shortages, soldiers being trained to operate some of the new tractors that had been imported. The new Women's Land Army also provided extra labour. Politicians then made a worrying discovery. High prices might get a stack threshed sooner, but the only way to get more grain to thresh was to plant more seed and be prepared to wait until it had grown and was fit to be harvested. The various steps taken did provide useful lessons for World War 2.

The same high prices stimulated production on the Canadian Prairies and in the United States. With the end of the war in 1918 promises were made in the Wheat Act that high prices would continue. Filled with optimism, farmers invested heavily in improving their farms. However, within two years the legislation had been repealed and cheap grain could once again be imported. By the time the crops that had been sown on the strength of solemn promises had been threshed, grain prices started to fall. This marked the start of another serious decline in British farming that was not reversed until World War 2 increased the demand for home-grown food.

2. INFLUENCES FROM ABROAD, 1920-39

As we have seen, at the end of the war promises had been made that prices would remain high and farming prosperous, but grain prices declined during the 1920s. Within a few years cheap imports had exposed the hollow nature of the politicians' promises, and large numbers of farmers cut their costs by reverting to growing grass.

With less cereals being grown, threshing contractors had less work. This reduced their need for new machinery and trade was very slow for agricultural engineers, many of whom had expanded due to the wartime demand. Their high costs meant that many were facing financial difficulties.

Typical was Clayton & Shuttleworth, which produced a number of prototype combines in 1928.

While they were offered in Britain, the main intention would have been to supply overseas markets where the company was well respected. But by 1930 it had gone, with little more than the Clayton name being purchased by Marshalls of Gainsborough.

Yet by the early 1930s it was estimated that there were some 50 imported combine harvesters of different makes in the country, but not all of them were in use every year. By 1935 one Norfolk farm was handling its entire harvest with two Massey Harris trailed combines. The arrival of a combine

A drawing of an International binder. While American binders cut on the left, English-made examples cut on the right. Thus the two types go round a field in opposite directions. You can imagine the problems for a farmer with one of each type!

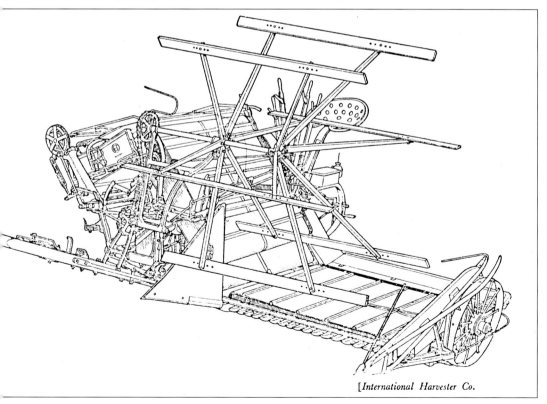

[*International Harvester Co.*

29

Left: Two views of an Albion binder, built in Lancashire. In the working position most binders were too wide to move easily, so to reduce the width in order to pass through gateways the binder could be lifted clear of the ground and fitted with a pair of transport wheels. An extra wooden drawbar was fitted through the cutter bar wheel and into a clip under the platform. With the drive wheel retracted the machine was ready to move. Removing two of the sails further reduced the overhang. When in work the mechanism was driven by the bull wheel just visible underneath. Soon combines would also need special travel arrangements to cope with narrow lanes and gateways.

Above: With the transport wheels removed the binder is prepared for work. The cutter bar mechanism is little different from that found on a combine, and the cut crop is transported sideways on top of the canvas belt braced with wooden slats.

meant that a farmer had grain to sell perhaps six months earlier than if he had to wait to get it threshed, which did help his cash flow. As more of the machines came into use, more and more farmers tried to sell grain straight off the combine. When combines became more common by the 1950s, this desire to sell usually resulted in the lowest prices being offered at harvest time.

Early customers for combines included enterprising young farmers who were acquiring large tracts of land very cheaply or at very low rents. Typically these were farms that had fallen derelict when the occupants had lost money during the 1920s.

Much the same was happening in the US and Canada. As well as falling prices, many farmers were hit by soil erosion caused by droughts, wind or floods. Smaller farms were absorbed by bigger operations, and these were potential customers for combines. Even with falling prices, grain growing on a large scale could still be profitable. Hot, dry growing conditions produced varieties of wheat in demand for bread-making, but carried to an extreme these conditions led to summer droughts, failed crops and dust storms where precious topsoil was blown away by strong winds.

In the United States combine development had been rapid. The monster land-wheel-driven machines were being faced with competition from rather smaller machines. The typical machine of the early 1930s was trailed; it carried its own petrol engine to drive the machinery, and travelled on three broad iron wheels, most of the weight being carried over the rear pair, while the single front wheel was on a turntable able to steer the combine as it followed the tractor. The cutter bar was hinged to the right side of the machine and was braced into the crop by a

31

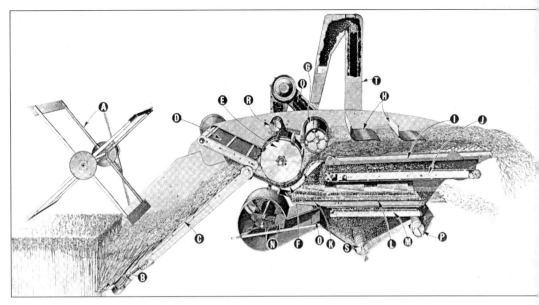

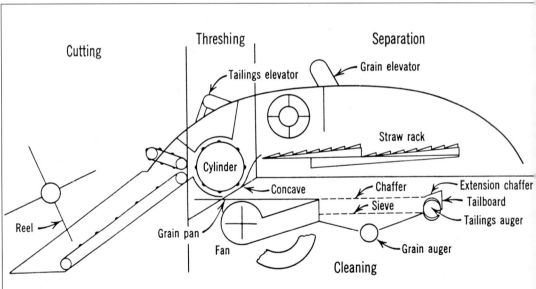

The layout of the main components of a trailed combine in cut-away and diagrammatic form. Compared with a threshing machine the grain is less tightly graded, but the other main functions are present. The crop is cut at B and conveyed up by the elevator C until guided in by conveyor D. E is the drum that threshes against the concave before throwing out a mat of straw passing under guides H over the straw walkers to discharge at the back. Rubbish in the grain is blown out by fan N, leaving the grain to work its way down through the sieves. Anything not properly threshed is caught by auger P to elevator Q to be discharged by auger R back into the drum. Good grain goes up elevator T for bagging or into the bin.

substantial triangular outrigger from the main structure of the machine. Another large wheel supported this outrigger. For travel the whole cutter bar and outrigger assembly could be folded vertically. Harvested grain was carried in a high-level tank. These trailed combines carried a supervisor to set the controls and ensure that the machine was working satisfactorily, leaving the driver to concentrate on the tractor.

Where grain was unloaded in bulk it could be transported direct to a local elevator where it would be graded and purchased outright. Some models had a bagging-off platform where a team sacked off the grain and secured the bags by tying or sewing the neck. International offered an arrangement whereby a bulk trailer was towed as the whole outfit was moving along, into which the grain could fall.

The threshing mechanism was still essentially a modified version of the well-proven separator. Although these machines were big, clumsy, and needed several operators, they transformed the economics of harvesting. There was no need for carting gangs for the sheaves, no need for the hired-in threshing machine, no need to cook meals for extra hired hands, and no need to recruit so many hired hands. This of course led to big savings in costs.

Australian farmers had gone for a different harvesting technique, whereby strippers combed most of the grain from the standing plant. This did away with the cutter bar and the need to pass the straw through the machine. Because the harvesting seasons were roughly six months apart, Australian and American harvester manufacturers did some of their testing and sales in each other's territories. As well as giving quicker results, sales went some way to balance demand.

As the market developed for combine harvesters other manufacturers realised that there was potential demand for smaller machines. An early pioneer in this area was the trailed Allis Chalmers All Crop Harvester. This was a total contrast to the big Rumley combines, which Allis Chalmers had continued to

offer after taking over the Rumley Company. Like other manufacturers, its bigger trailed harvesters were developed from the separators, which it was already manufacturing.

Cheaper versions of the All Crop were powered by a power take-off (PTO) from the towing tractor, and the engine speed of the tractor determined the speed at which the combine mechanism was driven. Meshed gears linked the PTO and the tractor's final drive; once a particular gear was selected, that and the engine speed determined the forward speed of the tractor and combine. For practical purposes this was the only forward speed where the combine mechanism was driven at the correct speed. Driven any faster, the threshing drum would crack the grain and the fans would blow good grain to waste out of the combine. If the speed fell, there was the risk of the combine blocking and the sieves choking. Few tractors offered more than two gear ratios suitable for combining.

If an auxiliary engine was fitted, both the gears and the tractor throttle could be used to control the forward speed. With the combine's separate engine running at the recommended speed, the combine could be kept loaded to its maximum throughput, increasing the daily output.

Whether or not to have a separate engine on a trailed combine became a popular debate. At first it was generally accepted that an engine would increase the cost, but also increase output. Storing and maintaining the engine would increase the servicing

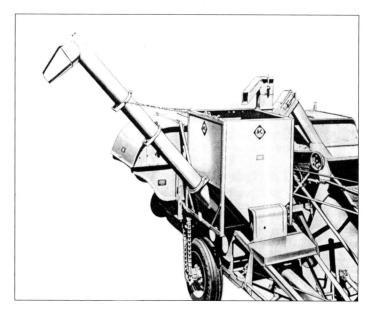

The All Crop 60: the grain tank was right over the transport axle, but the designers ensured that the weight of loose grain made little difference to how it towed.

needed. The debate was about whether the benefits outweighed the extra cost.

Long after trailed harvesters had gone out of fashion, modern tractors started another argument. A modern tractor could feed far more power into the PTO than the engine used by the combine-maker, and this extra power, combined with a larger choice of gears, meant that a trailer harvester could achieve an even higher output if PTO-driven.

However, researchers in Canada later added another strand to the argument. Massey Ferguson offered a trailed version of its big 760 combine, which for all practical purposes was identical to the self-propelled version. Try as they might, the researchers could not achieve as high an output from the trailed machine as the self-propelled. Much of the difference was attributed to the better driver position on the latter.

Meanwhile the Allis Chalmers All Crop defined a whole new market for combines. As its name implied, an All Crop could be adapted to harvest a wide range of different crops, and suitable tractors were widely available to pull it. From the beginning Allis Chalmers made the significant decision that All Crops would be produced in large numbers. Accordingly the factory was set up to produce them on an assembly-line basis, marking a change to mass production from individual machines being built and assembled by skilled craftsmen. The selling price could be set far lower, which increased the demand. For the first time it was realistic for a typical medium-sized farmer to contemplate buying a combine. On models equipped to handle grain in bulk, all the controls could be operated from the tractor seat, so only one tractor driver was needed to work the outfit. And being a much lighter design than any other manufacturer had offered, a smaller tractor could handle it.

After a series of different designs, what was recognised as the classic Model 60 All Crop entered production in 1935. The straw was conveyed upwards and backwards by a rubberised belt conveyor, presenting cut straw head first to the threshing drum. As this was mounted in line with the cutter bar, there was no need to move the straw sideways after cutting, which produced an excellent feed straight into the drum. Another unusual feature of the threshing drum was that the rasp bars were surfaced with rubber, and had a slight twist rather like a cylinder lawnmower, so there was only a small amount of the rasp bar in contact with the concave at that any given moment. These features gave good output with even relatively low power applied to the threshing drum. The threshed straw was thrown out of the drum with the grain on to straw walkers and sieves mounted across the width of the machine. This transverse mounting meant that the threshed straw fell well clear of the area that had been cut.

However, the design did mean that the machine was remarkably wide. An advisory film made during the war by the National Institute of Agricultural Engineering laid great stress on the importance of removing gateposts even before you took delivery of your Allis Chalmers All Crop.

On the All Crop the optional auxiliary engine was the same unit used for the Allis Chalmers B tractor. However, there were practical disadvantages to this installation. Its position on the drawbar prevented a complete swing of the starting handle, so the engine had to be started by pulling the handle from the side over top dead centre. Any attempt to crank the engine in the conventional way inevitably resulted in skinned knuckles and much bad language!

The entire straw walking area, including fans and sieves at the back of the machine, was driven by one long V belt, Allis Chalmers having been involved in developing Texrope V belts. Some of the pulleys would run by contact with the front of the belt, and others by the back. When this system worked well it was quite satisfactory — until the belt came off! The cutter bar and drum were unaffected, so threshed straw was still being packed into the machine, and once a substantial blockage had formed inside the machine the threshing drum would choke. Overloaded, the engine driving the combine would stall. This could be prevented by an alert operator noticing the engine note changing; he had a few seconds to declutch before the engine stalled. On the particular combine with which the author was familiar, there was only one way to declutch quickly. The operator on the bagging-off platform had to sink to his knees facing back down the machine, and by kicking out with one leg the clutch lever could be pushed out of action just before the engine stalled.

If the engine stalled it was, like many small Allis Chalmers units, reluctant to restart until it cooled down. This could mean an unpleasant job clearing the blockage followed by a long break before combining could resume. However, despite its vices and peculiarities, the All Crop harvester was keenly sought by owners as it proved a reliable combine that was cheap to operate. For its cutting width it had a surprisingly good output.

Less common in Britain was the Allis Chalmers All Crop 40, which was of a straight-through design —

the straw was discharged in line with the cutter bar.

Probably the most important effect of the All Crop 50 was to show other potential manufacturers that there would be a huge demand for lightweight trailed combines, and within a few years it was facing competition. International, John Deere, Massey and Minneapolis Moline soon had their equivalents in production, also built on light and economical lines. Production of the All Crop lasted through into 1952, with some machines for the British market being assembled at Totton, Southampton, and Essendine, Lincolnshire.

In Germany the binder-maker Claas introduced its MDB, which was essentially a binder that threshed the crop before tying the threshed straw into sheaves. The first prototypes blew the light material and weed seeds into a following trailer, but this idea was quickly abandoned, although it would have overcome a big early objection to combines: few farmers liked the idea of blowing weed seeds back into the field.

Most early British customers chose bagger combines. All the crew needed to keep working were enough sacks and no breakdowns; the combines could be run for as many hours as possible, with filled bags dropped on the ground. The simplest way to collect the sacks then was to use existing trailers, but this was hard work, as often the existing farm trailers were quite high to load. On a big farm there were probably isolated buildings that could be used as temporary shelter for sacks of grain.

However, some early combines transported grain in bulk, and to unload them the combine had to be stopped. Once a suitable vehicle was parked alongside, grain was allowed to fall from an outlet into the transport vehicle, although shovelling might be needed to finish the job. One problem was that it was rare to find available transport with a grain-tight body, and the first year that a combine arrived on a particular farm all sorts of makeshift modifications might have to be made to move the grain. Typical would be nailing sacks or patches to seal gaps in the sideboards and tailboards of an existing trailer.

Preserved by the Science Museum and stored at its Wroughton outstation is one of the first International combines imported into Britain. Parked here without its header, its origins as a stationary thresher can be seen. Fittingly it was restored by the late Roy Johnson when he worked at the Museum. Roy's father worked for International as a combine specialist and could well have unpacked and built up this machine when new.

Above: The Claas MDB could almost be described as a binder with a threshing attachment. From the offside the cutter bar, sails and canvases could be a binder.

Below: The loose straw was carried up to the compact threshing assembly. Grain was bagged off at the platform while the straw travelled to a trusser.

Above: With a built-in trusser the MDB tied the threshed straw into bundles before discharge.

Below: This particular MDB was imported privately in the late 1930s for use in Scotland. Long after it was disused it was restored to full working order for the Scottish Agricultural Museum. From time to time it is borrowed by Claas for publicity purposes.

37

The next problem was what to do with the harvested grain. Unless it was harvested on a hot, dry day, it was likely to be too damp for long-term storage. Yet any sort of grain-drying installation was a fixed location, and carting all the grain to it for preparation and storage could cause delays and hold up the combine.

The starting point for grain dryers in Britain was work that had been carried out on grass-drying. An unlikely result of this was that Imperial Chemical Industries (ICI) became a leading manufacturer of grass-drying machines, and it was discovered that they could be adapted for drying grain in large quantities. At first they achieved an impressive output, but at high temperatures the grain got too hot and was damaged. This was particularly serious if the grain was needed for seed or malting to make beer.

Many of these first dryers were coke-fired, which appealed to gas companies, offering an outlet for coke in the summer when demand was lower. Oil-firing offered steadier temperature control and eliminated the regular job of stoking up the furnace.

Overall it was becoming accepted that a combine would make the harvest easier, but even in America it was not yet widely used. By the end of the 1930s in Britain most farmers still relied on binders and threshing machines, but in the next few years their outlook was to change sharply.

Left: Up-to-date harvest transport of the 1930s: the Fordson tractor is supplied with the then new pneumatic tyres, which have been replaced with a later tread pattern. The trailer is built along the traditional lines of older wagons with a wooden chassis, but again fitted with pneumatic tyres. This outfit was ideal for carting sheaves at higher speeds than was possible with a horse-drawn wagon. It could also be used to deliver a load of grain in sacks to the local station or merchant.

Above: One of the first MDBs in use in Germany being pulled by a Lanz Bulldog tractor and driven by the power take-off (PTO). Could the crew have imagined how the Claas company would grow over the next 60 years? *J. Mann*

3. THE IMPACT OF WORLD WAR 2, 1939-45

In Britain World War 2 once again jolted the Government. Submarine activity and shortages of shipping capacity meant that increased food production was going to be vital. Lessons had been learned from World War 1, and the need for greater home food production was realised from the beginning.

By now there were several makes of small trailer combines in production in America that could be imported, including Allis Chalmers, John Deere, Massey Harris, International and Minneapolis. For example, Jack Oldings of Hertfordshire imported the John Deere 12A combine harvester as part of the John Deere range. This was a 6-foot-cut, straight-through trailed machine. Oldings also sold Caterpillar tracklayers, but a few years previously Caterpillar had sold much of its combine business to John Deere. Allis Chalmers was in Abbeydore, Herefordshire, and could offer the All Crop, while Sale Tilney offered

For a long time there was debate on the best way to turn a corner when towing a binder or trailed combine. Method (a) was neat but imposed a strain on the PTO drive while turning. With a binder, sheaves on the ground could be in the way. Method (b) involved reversing, and with PTO-driven equipment this meant that the drive had to be stopped twice during gear changing, imposing more wear and tear. Method (c) looked slipshod but was actually the quickest and imposed the least wear on the machine being towed. The arrival of self-propelled machines offered further possibilities.

three models of Minneapolis Moline 'Harvester' combines.

Researchers had been looking at the damage done to grain by combines, and judged that all makes were capable of producing a reasonable sample. The main cause of excess damage was incorrect settings by the operator.

Hard-pressed farmers were impressed by American estimates of the time needed to harvest an acre. By their figures it took about 50 man-hours to harvest and thresh an acre of grain with sickle and flail, while using a binder and thresher took 3 man-hours. With a trailed combine harvester it took something less than an hour. At first sight that suggests a 50-fold improvement over manual methods, but with hindsight the researchers probably overlooked that with the first two methods the threshed straw and bagged grain were left where they were needed instead of still in the field.

In 1939 two million extra acres were ploughed out of grass, and most were planted to cereals or potatoes. Wartime needs led to a tenfold increase in combines during the war. These statistics cover a lot of sudden and unexpected changes coped with by farmers and their support industries.

Strict controls were introduced on new machines. Whether it was a threshing machine or a combine, it was allocated where it was thought it would do most good. This job fell to 'War Ags', county-based

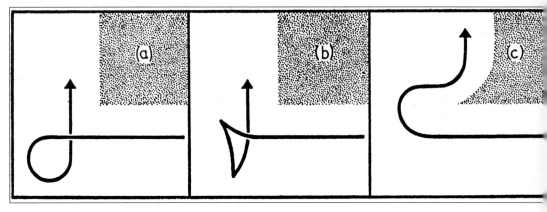

committees answering to the Minister of Agriculture and charged with the job of increasing food production. More formally known as the County War Agricultural Executive Committees, they were first seen during World War 1. Allocations might be to their own machinery pool or to somebody with a reputation as an energetic contractor. Many of these early contractors would continue to offer a contract service after the wartime emergency had ended.

Finding enough men to use a threshing machine was a problem. Perhaps three men were required to pitch sheaves to the drum and at least one man to bag the grain, although it really needed two to ensure that each bag was weighed and the contents adjusted before being tied off. Then the filled sacks had to be transported for storage in a barn or granary, which might need a couple more men and maybe a horse and cart. Getting the weed seeds and cavings away from the drum required two more. Even if the contractor supplied an elevator or baler, two more men would be needed to deal with the loose straw. Another horseman would be needed on the water cart to supply the engine with water. At a minimum, that suggested a gang of eight to ten plus the contractor's men. The contractor would supply two men with the drum, and the rest would be made up first with farm

staff, then perhaps neighbours helping in return for help with their own threshing. Another source was casual independent workers. While not employed by the contractor, they would be well known to him and willing to be called on as required. These varied from fit and skilful to near useless, and the farmer would pay them each day. In much the same way, a contractor today, combining a farm, might suggest suitable drivers to help with carting the grain. Girls from the Land Army or, later, Prisoners of War often covered wartime shortages.

Other equipment might be supplied to work with the threshing machine. An elevator lifted threshed straw high in the air, dropping it towards the centre of the stack. A trusser would tie the straw into handy bundles. A wire baler produced heavy but weather-resistant, bales. While awkward to handle, each bale

Reffolds was one of the less well-known manufacturers of balers. Built in 1930, this example worked in Boston, Lincolnshire, until 1960, packing straw tightly into wire-tied high-density bales. Such dense bales permitted bigger and heavier loads to be carried, and straw merchants in particular valued the savings thus made possible. In the same way today they offer a premium for big rectangular high-density bales. The baler is taking part in a working demonstration at Much Marcle Steam Rally in Herefordshire.

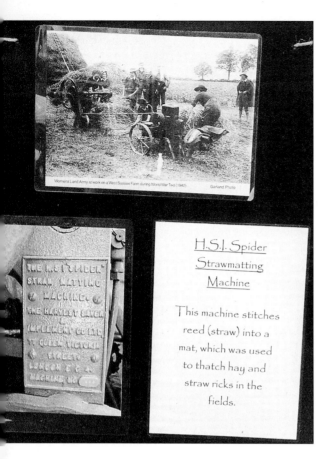

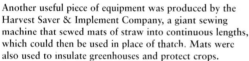

H.S.I. Spider
Strawmatting
Machine

This machine stitches
reed (straw) into a
mat, which was used
to thatch hay and
straw ricks in the
fields.

Another useful piece of equipment was produced by the Harvest Saver & Implement Company, a giant sewing machine that sewed mats of straw into continuous lengths, which could then be used in place of thatch. Mats were also used to insulate greenhouses and protect crops.

A preserved HSI matting machine driven by a Wolseley engine. In front of the machine is a short length of the matting it produces. Skilled thatchers were hard to find in wartime and many stacks were successfully protected by mats produced by unskilled teams of Land Girls.

held a lot of straw, which was particularly useful if straw was to be moved off the farm. A big chaff-cutter could produce the straw ready chopped for bedding or feeding. These 'extras' could affect the number of men needed to do the job.

Another consideration was when to thresh. Threshing straight after harvest meant that the grain was ready to sell or use sooner. On the other hand, the men might be better used getting on with the winter ploughing. Since most neighbours also wanted to thresh later, how could the contractor fit it all in? As he was keen to save time and money on moves he would try to persuade adjoining farms to accept consecutive dates. While wartime controls lasted, the Machinery Officer of the local War Ag had powers to monitor and direct contractors as to when and where

they threshed. Most farmers had to register in advance with a particular contractor.

From the contractor's point of view he would like to get all the threshing done in one visit, but the farmer might prefer several visits to reduce pressure on storage facilities and to avoid neglecting other jobs while threshing. Therefore planning his round involved considerable diplomacy on the part of the contractor — he had to convince all his customers that their work was getting top priority. Often it was the contractor's wife who took their agitated phone calls. In peacetime, after a few years, an established contractor would be able to work out a round and virtually tell customers when they were to have their corn threshed. An efficient contractor would be able to get six months or more work out of his threshing drums each year. As they were robust machines he could also look forward to a long working life before they needed replacement. By contrast, a combine worked for only a few weeks each year, with many components to wear.

A farmer's choice of contractors would normally be limited to those that operated from a base within cycling range of the farm. However, to meet the wartime emergency some crews travelled much further, lodging locally.

Although threshing contractors did meet a need for cereal growers, it was not the perfect system, and growers could see the advantages of the combine harvester when it became available to them. Often, however, the combine would be hired from a forward-looking threshing contractor who realised that times were changing.

So what made a successful contractor? Above all a willingness to work long and hard. A typical contractor led by example: if threshing was due to start at 8 in the morning he would be getting up steam at 6, uncovering the threshing drum, and lubricating round so that at 8am the equipment was ready for work. The two crucial jobs were operating the steam engine and feeding the sheaves into the

threshing drum. Effectively the feeder was the captain of the crew. He needed a constant supply of sheaves correctly presented to feed the maximum amount of material into the drum. Yet if the chap sacking off the grain or the boy clearing the rubbish from under the machine did not keep up with the output, their neglect could choke his machine. Some of his team would be casual workers who followed the drum from farm to farm — farm staff could not be abused quite so readily!

Mechanical skills would also be displayed, listening to every squeak, rattle and hum on the machine. Whether a minor adjustment, lubrication, or a more drastic repair was needed, the threshing contractor was the one to do it. If it were humanly possible a repair would be carried out without stopping threshing, even if it meant working through the night.

In use, the working platform of the threshing machine extends out over the drive belt to give the feeder and his helper room to move and space for the pitchers to place sheaves. Notice the unguarded belt at head height for anybody working with the sacks on the back of the drum. Endless belts were used to reduce the risk of injury from a passing belt fastener, and were usually crossed to give more grip on the small pulley.

The undisputed boss of the machine was the feeder man on the threshing drum. He set the pace of work, exhorting slackers and perhaps changing the team round to achieve the highest output. On top of the working platform is a reed comber, an extra attachment that removes short lengths of straw so that after threshing the straw will be unbroken for use on thatched roofs.

Even today, the successful contractor mostly still leads by example. He is good at both motivating his staff and overcoming any obstacle that prevents getting the job done. Technology has made a difference, however: once a loud shout was useful, but today it is often a case of ringing mobile phones.

Once they had got their own work done, farmers with combines were encouraged to undertake contract work for neighbours. Farmers were eager to take advantage of this labour-saving machine. Labour was short and the controlled prices for cereals were very acceptable.

The arrival of a combine harvester posed a number of problems before farmers could use it. The first and most obvious was what were they going to do with the grain produced by the combine. Sacks were a simple and effective answer for storing grain, especially if it was sold soon after combining. One big difference between British and American conditions was the prospect of wet weather during harvest.

Harvested grain will only store for long periods if it can be held below a certain critical combination of temperature and moisture content; the cooler the grain the higher the moisture content at which it can be stored. Unfortunately, if the grain does start to deteriorate it warms up, which in turn increases the rate at which it deteriorates. Without some means of drying grain a farmer could only harvest it at a sufficiently low moisture content to be able to store it safely.

The British climate meant that weather conditions typically deteriorated as harvest progressed. Waiting to harvest grain when it was dry enough to store could result in a combine not being used when neighbours were able to continue harvesting. At the beginning of the harvest, grain might be left because it was likely to be too wet. By the end of the harvest the combine was often working under even worse conditions, which could be the only way of completing a harvest. Bringing in a binder to harvest a crop so much later in the year could result in serious losses of grain during cutting.

The farmer who harvested grain that was too wet to store had a problem. One answer was to sell it quickly to a merchant willing to accept damp grain, but this was possible if the grain was only slightly wet. To cover his trouble the merchant would impose

A farm's supply of sacks could be supplemented by hired or other used sacks to form a simple and effective storage and transport method.

This enamel sign still to be seen in Pewsey, Wiltshire, was once a familiar sight to farmers seeking sacks for hire. Hired sacks offered a predictable storage cost per week, and most buyers would accept delivery in them. The sacks would be returned off hire as soon as they were emptied.

An effective way to store empty sacks out of reach of rats and mice was to hang them from a beam.

a heavy deduction for drying costs and weight loss of the grain when dried. During the wartime period merchants were less fussy and price controls limited the deductions they could make, but in later years damp grain would make the farmer a very weak seller and tended to result in lower prices for his grain.

To prevent harvested grain escaping official controls, combine owners, like threshing contractors, were expected to report all grain harvested or threshed over the previous week. At first reports went to the Ministry of Food, but later to the local War Ag. A separate form required details of the fields where crops had been harvested. Separately the County Machinery Officer insisted that intentions for the next week had to be advised in a weekly report.

Other wartime regulations were introduced to reduce or prevent losses. Stacks being threshed had to be surrounded by a mouse-proof barrier, typically wire netting to prevent their escape. Most threshing contractors would have a couple of fearless terriers that would make short work of rats and mice when they showed themselves.

Many farm workers tied each trouser leg below the knee with string to keep the knee baggy when bending their legs. For threshing, more string might be used to tie trousers even lower down to prevent rats and mice even starting the climb! Sometimes a farm 'humorist' would catch a mouse and insert it into the clothing of an unsuspecting helper. Their reaction provided the rest of the team with a good laugh as a brief respite from hard work.

The coming of combines changed the situation for rodents. Now the harvested grain was taken straight from the field, and all that was left for them was the grain lost during harvest, any spillage, and any unthreshed grain left in the straw.

Incendiary bombs were an added wartime hazard. The 'Siting of Ricks Regulations of 1942' stipulated that stacks should be at least 20 yards from any building or other stack, although it was permitted to build stacks in pairs for ease of threshing. As a result, some stacks were built in locations that proved impossible to reach with a threshing machine. Enemy action could be more direct — at least one civilian collected a medal for bravery for continuing to feed a threshing machine while under enemy fire.

When America joined in the fighting, it put the United States on a war footing, and like all agricultural machinery manufacturers, Massey Harris was rationed for materials. At the same time the emphasis was being switched to munitions, yet

Massey Harris had a revolutionary new combine. Like other big manufacturers of binders it had introduced a trailed combine, but its new self-propelled machine had the cutter bar mounted at the front. For the first time here was a combine harvester that could be driven straight into a field to start work without knocking over and damaging any grain or straw in the field. Normally, to avoid this damage, most farmers would still have the first swathe around a field cut with a scythe, with the sheaves hand-tied in the traditional manner. This left a clear swathe for the tractor pulling the binder or combine.

As in Britain, American farmers responded to the war effort by increased plantings. Yet farm boys were in the Forces rather than waiting to help with the harvest, and the Massey combines sold in Texas, Oklahoma and Kansas had already headed north, cutting the previous year's crops. Through the negotiating skills of Vice-President Joe Tucker, Massey Harris received sanction to build 500 of its new No 21 combines.

These were not, however, to be put on general sale. Instead Massey Harris undertook that they would be used to harvest crops throughout the US as they came ripe. The initial commitment was to harvest at least one square mile (640 acres) of crops with each machine. For publicity purposes they were referred to as the 'Harvest Brigade'.

The new combines were supplied to experienced operators who collected them in the Southern States, and during the next few months, starting with early-ripening crops in California, they worked their way north, travelling all but very short distances on lorries.

When the results were totalled up it was calculated that over a million acres had been harvested in just under a quarter of a million combine running hours. That gave a true average of over 4 acres per hour. The top 10 per cent of machines had harvested over 2,500 acres apiece, which was good going for a 14-foot direct-cut header.

A lot of planning went into achieving such a creditable result. Massey Harris sales offices (branch houses) co-ordinated back-up from dealers, and the various State and Federal agricultural agencies did their bit to keep the combines gainfully occupied.

Custom cutters still follow the same practice today. Travelling in teams, they cut their way north, often into Canada, so that their customers can manage without combines, grain transport or skilled employees. Many of the drivers are farmers' sons keen to earn good pay for long hours.

Above: Pioneer of the self-propelled combine was the Massey Harris 21, early examples of which were built using galvanised steel. Controls were basic, with a vertical steering column and a second wheel to control the height of the cut. Mounted in front of the cutter bar is a pick-up reel for swathed crops. Behind and above the driving seat is the housing for the rotary screen, which feeds down to the bagging-off spouts.

Below: A close-up of the pick-up arrangement on the Massey Harris 21. It used two canvases like those on binders, which brought the straw towards the centre of the header after the crop had been lifted up and on to the header.

Above: The vertical wheel on the Massey Harris 21 combine controlled the height of the cutter bar. A brake arrangement helped to reduce unwanted movement.

Below: The 21's Chrysler petrol engine was mounted low down behind the drive axle, where it could pick up plenty of straws and dust, increasing the fire risk. If the drive chain broke, the brakes were ineffective and there was a serious risk of the combine running away.

Today, several East Anglia steam rallies try and include some space for a working demonstration of combines. This Massey Harris 21 is parked having harvested its allocated area at the Weeting Steam Rally.

With the introduction of the Massey Harris 21 the main features of a self-propelled combine design became established. The transmission was arranged so that the driver had the choice of a considerable number of different speeds even without changing the speed of the engine. This transmission layout used the idea of the variable-diameter V belt pulley. A moulded endless V belt was mounted on two special pulleys, and the spacing of the two sheaves of the pulley could be altered. When close together the belt would run as though on a large-diameter pulley, but when the pulley sheaves were further apart the diameter would effectively become much smaller. By altering those two diameters a considerable difference in speed ratio between the two pulleys could be obtained. The driver controlled the sheaves on one pulley, while the other was under spring tension. While this tended to close the sheaves, this was opposed by belt tension. With the sheaves eased right off, the belt could not be driven at all, providing a form of clutch. In this state the engine could continue to drive the threshing and cutting mechanism, allowing the machine to clear itself.

The belt drive was fitted between the engine and the gearbox. While it meant that the belt ran faster, it reduced the load on the belt. This ingenious transmission allowed the petrol engine to be mounted crossways and almost between the front wheels. In practice this meant that in use the engine could be run continuously at its normal governed running speed. A gear was first selected with a conventional gear lever, while moving a large lever over a quadrant altered the position of the sheaves. In turn this altered the effective ratio between the engine speed and gearbox input. Within a gear, such speed changes could be made on the move. The driver was thus able to make all important speed and height adjustments from the driving seat. Raising and lowering the cutter bar was done by a large hand wheel, which could be checked by use of the external brake.

Steering of the combine was by the rear axle, which carried a relatively small proportion of the machine's total weight. The front, driven, wheels were shod with tractor-type tyres offering a good combination of grip and load-carrying capacity. On the 21, cut straw was transported to the centre of the cutter bar where it could be fed into the threshing drum mechanism. On the early models this was done with canvases running on rollers in much the same way as binders had operated. Once the straw was fed into the drum the rest of the treatment was not that much different from a conventional threshing machine. Threshed grain either flowed into sacks or into a bulk container fitted with a power-driven discharge auger. This meant that it was able to discharge its load on the move, which required some accurate driving of the tractor and trailer outfit running alongside. The tractor driver had to be alert for the combine suddenly stopping due to a blockage. Missing the warning signs could mean that the trailer was no longer under the auger. Result? A large quantity of grain discharged on to the ground! Early 21s were built using galvanised sheet and supplied unpainted but very well protected. Material shortages later forced a change to painted but unprotected sheet metal.

In Britain the self-propelled Massey Harris opened up completely new possibilities for contractors. Here was a machine that could be driven from farm to farm at quite a reasonable speed. Arriving at a new farm it could start work as soon as it got through the gate, provided that the weather conditions were suitable.

Contractors were allocated many of these early machines, which meant that many farmers could gain the benefit of using a combine harvester without waiting to purchase a new machine. As the new machines were in short supply, even those farmers who could afford to purchase might not have been allocated a combine.

By working long hours, contractors were able to deal with the requirements of many farmers. Unlike the 'Harvest Brigade' their combines usually stayed in one locality. Variations in soil type, ripening dates and varieties meant that a contractor was kept busy for several weeks, and blackout regulations prevented much useful work after dark.

Wartime demands meant that many farmers were growing grain crops for the first time in several years, the War Ag having probably directed them to do so. Quite reasonably, they may well have looked to the War Ag for harvest help, many being unable to get their crops combined. Wartime expansion meant that there was still plenty of work for binders. Such farmers still relied on threshing contractors, but even here there could be surprises. Instead of a steam engine there could be a powerful American tractor pulling and driving the outfit. This allowed the former steam engine driver to leave the tractor running unattended while concentrating on supervising the drum. In turn his former mate could take charge of an additional tractor and threshing drum outfit. Wartime labour shortages could mean that the threshing team might be of mixed sex or even an all-female Land Army team — highly regarded by many farmers. Some combines were used to replace a conventional threshing machine, and while this would work, clearing the threshed straw could be more difficult with a low outlet.

In typical British fashion, farms thus muddled through and kept the country fed while the war was won.

4. POSTWAR SHORTAGES, 1945-50

Farming had come through the war, and belatedly both the Government and town-dwellers had realised that it was only farm production that had avoided mass starvation. But farmers were still wary. After World War 1 the same sort of praise had been heaped on their heads, and extravagant promises had been made that prices would remain high. They had been told then that it would pay to continue growing the cereals the country needed, but within two years prices had collapsed.

With events like that within the memory of many farmers, there was natural caution about future prospects. There were, however, big differences; with the need to make substantial dollar repayments to the United States, there were few dollars to buy grain. The ravages of war meant that mainland Europe was in no position to supply food — indeed, it needed food from Britain — and many traditional exporting industries had lost their customary overseas markets. Foreign currency was in short supply, and home-grown food could reduce the need for it.

The 1948 Agriculture Act laid down a basis of guaranteed prices for farm produce including cereals. For the first time in peacetime farmers could be confident of the price they would receive for a crop before planting. Most employees of War Ag Committees were re-employed in the peacetime National Agricultural Advisory Service, whose aim was to encourage the growth of crops by better technical advice. Many of these advisers were well aware of the benefits of combine harvesting and were well placed to advise their farmers.

Confident of demand, farmers were willing to invest in new technology such as the combine harvester, and demand far exceeded supply. Eager buyers would chase even a second-hand trailed combine, and several contractors recall epic tractor drives. Even a worn-out combine harvester was a welcome addition.

Dollar shortages meant that it was no longer practical to import combine harvesters from the United States, so makers were encouraged to set up manufacturing facilities in Britain. As well as supplying Britain they could supply other countries in the 'Sterling area', which broadly comprised the British Empire. There they would also benefit from lower import duties compared with American-built machinery. Some, like Massey Harris, Allis Chalmers and International Harvester, rose to the challenge and set up branch factories. Others, such as John Deere, Minneapolis Moline and Oliver, withdrew from the British market. In Germany Claas was re-establishing production.

Massey Harris assembled some 21s imported from kits before starting to manufacture the 726 combine. In early publicity, driving a self-propelled combine was likened to driving a lorry. In that period power steering on a lorry was unknown, and few had any form of power-assisted brakes, while adjustments needed a strong arm. Probably the first example of power assistance came with the electric lift offered on the Massey Harris 726, where a flick of a switch would raise or lower the cutter bar, although this depended on a well-charged battery and the assister springs being correctly adjusted.

The power unit remained low down at the front but was now either a Morris (side valve) or Austin (overhead valve) lorry engine fitted with a governor. Most also had a vaporiser so that they could run on cheaper paraffin rather than petrol. International concentrated on tractor production at first, but would shortly commence production of its B64 trailed harvester. Allis Chalmers took over premises that had previously belonged to Minneapolis Moline at Essendine near Stamford in Lincolnshire, allowing the company to move from Totton, Southampton. As well as tractor production, the All Crop 60 harvester was assembled using some components imported from the United States. While this presented Massey Harris with a monopoly in self-propelled combines, it did at least make it possible to source British-built combines. Binders were imported from Germany where both Lanz and Claas were encouraged to supply the British market.

Left: The Massey Harris 726 was the first self-propelled combine on many farms. Notice the complete absence of guards for the drive chains. The engine lurks in the black hole behind the white battery.

Below left: A rear view of the bagging-off arrangements on a newly restored British-built Massey Harris 726. Again a rotary screen feeds down to the bagging-off spouts; underneath is a seat that can be pivoted out to form the back of the bagging platform, and held in place by the other length of angle iron running from the sacking-off point. Empty sacks would be draped over this. The nearest outlet is for reject grain, so this sack would fill relatively slowly, yet all the filled sacks had to be dragged past this obstacle to reach the chute. Production ceased in 1953.

Above right: A close-up of the electric lift used on the 726 combine. The electric motor drives a worm gearbox which in turn drives a chain linked to the big wheel sector. This represented the first power assistance for combine drivers.

Right: For complicated machines like the 726, customers would require spare parts and, to aid ordering, comprehensive spare parts lists were supplied to dealers. Customer and storeman would pore over these exploded drawings trying to identify the replacement bits the customer urgently needed. Each number relates to a description and part number listed on the adjoining page. For example, No 51 relates to Screen 636 760 M92 No 52 Extension, while the Screen No 52 is one digit different, 636 860 M92. Assembled, they mount on shaft 38 inside the housing 1. As they rotate slowly, grain inside passes out of the appropriate perforations to fall through the correct outlet if slide 118 is up. In the waste industry, devices like this are on a much larger scale and known as trommels.

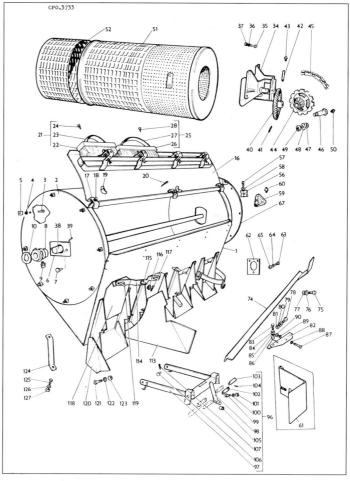

Above: The Allis Chalmers All Crop 60's auxiliary engine was the same as that used for the B tractor. The design of drawbar made it impossible to crank in the orthodox way, but despite minor grumbles it was an excellent machine and many young contractors worked them hard while building up their businesses. A very worthwhile modification was the rope to the clutch lever, which allowed the tractor driver to declutch the engine without leaving the tractor.

Left: In Germany Claas had resumed production of trailer combines, the Super replacing the MDB. This is an early postwar Claas Super combine with the cutter bar folded, making it compact for travelling. Before folding, the reel was removed and stowed on the combine behind the bagging platform.

With demand strong, little thought was given to servicing with these early designs. It was taken for granted that wherever grease was needed that was where a grease nipple was fitted. The challenge for the combine operator was to find the concealed nipples. Once found, it was often a case of the driver operating a mechanism to bring each one to a position where the grease-gun could be applied, meanwhile getting filthy with dust and prickles. It was claimed that finding all the grease nipples ensured that the combine was thoroughly inspected every day! In the real world it meant that some operators ignored a nipple that was particularly hard

An all-Marshall threshing outfit. The belt drives the end of the drum that does the threshing, while at the base is the fan that blows grain through the sieve to remove the light waste. As it is still used for preparing thatching straw it carries one or two unusual modifications. The wheels are ex-military, making transport easier than with the original steel wheels. While this restored Marshall Agricultural Engine probably powered a threshing machine during its working life, it is rather older than this late-model all-steel threshing drum. These were the final type of threshing machine used on English farms.

to get at, and this neglect might later reveal itself as a failure at the most inconvenient time. Typical awkward locations would be the nipples on elevators, straw walkers and idler sprockets.

Even with a combine on the farm there remained the problem of transporting the grain after it had been harvested. Faced with bulk discharge from a combine, many farms found themselves with trailers that did not tip. Often for the first unprepared season grain had to be shovelled out of the trailer, and working out some better arrangement was usually a priority job for the next winter.

Ferguson had just introduced its hydraulic tipping trailer, which when new could easily be made grain-tight. If the grain could be tipped into a pit at the store, grain carting became a relatively easy job. Such trailers were still, however, in short supply and only really suitable to be pulled by a Ferguson tractor.

Lorries were sometimes pressed into service, including redundant military lorries often carrying General Service bodies, which could be made grain-tight even if they did not tip. Haulage contractors could also be used to help with transport.

Taking an idea from American-style separators, the top-quality grain is fed by elevator into the back of a lorry converted into a bulk carrier with a plastic sheet. The aluminium ladder is another modern improvement. The Marshall agricultural engine both powered the machine in use and towed it from farm to farm.

Since many tractors still had no hydraulic system, some trailers were tipped manually using hand-cranked screw mechanisms. If hydraulics were used, a hand pump was provided on each trailer, but both versions were much harder work than the fingertip action of the Ferguson.

In addition, the arrival of the first imported pick-up balers offered a quicker and easier way of collecting straw for later use.

Threshing contractors were not entirely forgotten. Marshalls of Gainsborough offered the Field Marshall, with the option of a protective canopy and a winch. This formed the logical replacement for a steam engine. As well as releasing a man and cutting

fuel costs, the Field Marshall did not need an early riser to light or stoke the boiler. Now we look back on steam with nostalgia, but at the time a tractor was welcomed. Meanwhile, as steel shortages permitted, makers were supplying all-steel drums to replace worn-out older machines.

The 1940s finished with plenty of demand, but still with a serious shortage of machines.

Right: The same maker, Marshalls of Gainsborough, introduced its short-lived trailed combine after World War 2. Powered by a Ford 10hp engine, it was substantially made in typical Britannia Works style, and weighed about 2½ tonnes. As well as a combine the designers felt that it could be used as a self-contained threshing machine. Like the first Claas there were twin wheels on the heavier, bagging side. The planned self-propelled version never got into production. Despite its neglected condition this example from the first batch is now in the hands of a well-known Marshall enthusiast who is likely to make a good job of the restoration.

5. COMBINES BECOME THE NORM, THE 1950s

Farmers needed no convincing of the benefits of combine harvesters. Demand was still outstripping supply, and more manufacturers started production, with importers helping to meet the demand with machines from continental Europe.

Early designers had relied on the driver's muscle-power, but to ease the load on the driver many manufacturers gradually introduced hydraulic assistance for various tasks. With the introduction of the Massey Harris 780 to replace the 726, raising and lowering the cutter bar was done hydraulically.

Further development at Marshalls produced the 626 trailed combine. The engine was repositioned, making for a tidier layout, and for transport the hitch could be set to one side using a link to reduce the overall width when travelling. Despite the company's long experience building threshing drums, these combines were not a commercial success. When Clayton & Shuttleworth closed down, Marshalls had bought the rights to the trading name, but there were no similarities in design to earlier Clayton & Shuttleworth combines.

Edward Humphries' business went on to become Fisher Humphries. This all-steel machine would have had a short working life, having been built in the 1950s when few farmers would be looking for a threshing drum, so sales were slow. Once a threshing machine seemed enormous, but this one fits comfortably on the demountable body of a modern lorry.

Sometimes only a relatively small addition to a tractor's hydraulic system was needed to make life easier on the farm. This simple and effective E. O. Culverwell sack-lifter works by being pinned to the lower link arms of the tractor, then being hooked under the link arms further forward, so effectively becoming a rigid extension of the hydraulic linkage. As such it provided welcome assistance in the harvest field.

The last Massey Ferguson 780 combines carried the early Massey Ferguson red and grey livery, and the Perkins L4 engine was mounted between and just behind the front wheels. As a result, the cut crop had to pass over the engine and into the threshing drum. The meshed tower on the left removed chaff from the air being drawn down to pass through the radiator. Normally a sack would be added and fitted around the top of these perforations to act as an additional filter. On the later Massey Ferguson 515 (right) a rotary filter was used. The yellow 'crescent' design produced a curious strobing effect when the harvester was in use.

On parade in Essex in 1999 is this Massey Ferguson 780 Special owned by artist Stephen Binks, who had first restored it to model for his print '60s Harvest'. At some time it has gained extension sides to increase the carrying capacity of the grain tank. As was so common, a waterproof sheet is neatly rolled ready to protect the machine when parked. The knack of folding the sheet was to arrange it so that it could be unrolled along the top, then opened out to cover the whole width. Since sheeting-up was often done as rain approached or as darkness was falling, this preplanning made the job easier.

Buyers had the option of the Perkins L4 diesel engine, which offered better fuel economy, reduced fire risk and gave superior lugging ability under difficult conditions. Since then the diesel engine has been the preferred power unit for most self-propelled combines, and is usually based on a current lorry or tractor engine with minor modifications for use as an industrial unit. By picking the right engine, farmers and dealers had the advantage of an established spares and service network.

A name change followed the take-over of Ferguson by Massey Harris. At first the clumsy 'Massey Harris Ferguson' name was used, but this was followed by the more familiar 'Massey Ferguson'. It also led to the abandonment of plans to mount a combine on a Ferguson 20 tractor. Test drivers reported that driver visibility was poor, and performance was limited by only one or two usable gear ratios for combining, heavy steering, overheating and dust blowing over the driver. Had development continued, with tractor design becoming more sophisticated, it could have proved cost-effective, but instead farmers with smaller acreages were offered the self-propelled Massey Ferguson 735. Towards the end of the decade the 780 was restyled as the Massey Ferguson 788.

The compact dimensions of the Massey Ferguson 735 are highlighted as it is transported on a car trailer. Introduced in the 1950s, the 735 was aimed at the smaller grower, and ease of transport made these machines very popular for harvesting trial plots in various parts of the country.

Waiting its turn to parade at the Great Dorset Steam Fair is a preserved Massey Ferguson 735 combine. The engine to the driver's right was a BMC 1500cc B series car engine fitted with a governor.

It was claimed that the 735's entire power pack could be removed and used as a stationary power unit when the combine was not in use.

A side view of the 735's bagging platform. One ingenious feature was the use of galvanised riddles. The unused sets were clipped in place for transport and served as guards.

An Allis Gleaner combine which, by an indirect route, would later give its name to the parent of the Massey Ferguson organisation.

Independently Danish manufacturer JF did offer a quite successful tractor-mounted combine, while other manufacturers introduced self-propelled machines, including Ransome's 902, with 10-foot or 12-foot cuts, and Allis Chalmers' Gleaner. In Germany Claas added the Self Propelled, Europa and Columbus combines to its trailer combine output. Also from Germany came two Lanz models, later to be better known as John Deeres. Jones Balers announced its short-lived Cruiser, the only Welsh-built combine. Bamford of Uttoxeter imported the Claeys combine; Leon Claeys was not connected with Claas, yet its M103 and M73 had many similarities to the equivalent Claas design. After a few years of confusion the Clayson name was adopted.

In 1955 David Brown Tractors bought Harrison McGregor & Guest Limited. Based at Leigh, Lancashire, it was the maker of Albion farm machines, including some 67,000 Albion binders. Production soon started at Leigh of the David Brown trailer combine; using a Swedish design, built under licence, it had a 5-foot cut and weighed about a tonne and a half. It was therefore aimed at the same market as the established Allis Chalmers All Crop 60. Other competitors were also appearing: Ransome offered the MST 56 of very similar specification, while the trailed International B64, with 6-foot cut, was slightly heavier. Importers were also able to offer the Swedish Aktiv.

With supply easing, farmers could be more discriminating in their buying. Once the initial demand for combines had been met, manufacturers found that they needed to *sell* rather than just accept orders. The supply of second-hand combines was also improving, so more farmers were able to consider buying a combine.

The problem of transporting grain in bulk was also beginning to be solved, and farms started to look for better trailers in order to accommodate larger quantities of grain. Larger farms might operate several combines to achieve the desired output. If several machines were working in a field it was always difficult to know which combine needed to empty its tank most urgently. Some farms devised a system of flags or signals so that the driver knew where to head. Unloading on the move kept the combine working, although some operators favoured stopping to empty the grain, which gave time for a quick look round the combine, and perhaps an early chance to detect faults.

Above: Claas started with trailer combines. This is a Super Automatic with bagging platform and trusser fitted. A throwback to the early reapers is the second man riding to poke free any blockages. *J. Mann*

Left: This Super Automatic is awaiting restoration. Like earlier American designs, the cutter bar could be folded up for transport. The half-tonne grain tank was carried up high, although a bagging platform could be supplied instead.

Below: At first glance the Super Automatic looks rather bulky, not helped by the high mounting position for the grain tank. This example is in the post-1953 green livery and is fitted with a trusser at the rear, which bunched and tied the threshed straw.

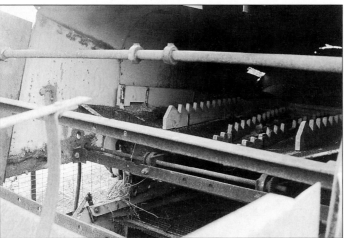

Above: The rotating auger acted as both a divider and to urge the crop in; much the same idea is used today on maize headers. The driver had hydraulic controls to raise and lower either the cutter bar or the reel. As this power was supplied from the combine, the tractor only needed a power take-off.

Left: Grain was threshed by the drum, mounted lengthways, after which the straw travelled back on these walkers, which were of a simple but effective design. The profiled timber was sufficient to carry the straw back while allowing the grain to drop out.

Left: Pressing the company name and address into a panel left no doubt as to who had built the combine.

Right: Claas introduced its Self Propelled combine in 1954. Powered by a Perkins L4 diesel engine, it was unsophisticated but effective. Many features of the SP design are now commonplace, for example the mounting of the engine high and out of the way, and the driver sitting centrally and out over the intake elevator. Mounting the tank almost over the front drive axles gave extra grip and minimal change in weight on the steering axle. The discharge auger could be folded back for travel.

Below: Driver comfort meant that the seat was supported on four coil springs!

Below right: To change gear the driver needed to leave his seat to use a short lever on the top of the gearbox. It probably meant slower movements within the field than today, but would have had little impact on overall output.

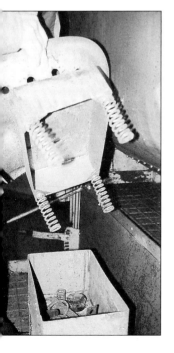

Above: Two early Claas Self Propelled combines hard at work. *J. Mann*

Below: A Claas trailed combine seen behind a Nuffield tractor. The Nuffield was particularly well suited to driving a trailed combine. When offered with a live PTO it was controlled by a separate hand clutch. This meant that the combine was driven at a constant speed without any risk of a break even when the driver changed gear. By the time live PTOs came into widespread use customers had tasted the other advantages of a self-propelled machine. *J. Mann*

A number of companies introduced what they called grain tanks, which would fit inside a trailer. Built up from sheet steel, they were leak-proof and emptied through a single hatch at the rear. Tamplins of Chichester introduced such tanks complete with tipping gear, which could be mounted on flat trailers or lorries, converting them to bulk tippers.

The Electrical Development Association became interested in the problem of drying grain, its research being focused on using large fans to drive plenty of air through the grain to remove moisture. Not surprisingly the Association favoured heating the air with electrical heater banks when conditions were unfavourable, the attraction being the opportunity to sell large quantities of electricity at a time of year when demand elsewhere was low. The nationalised Electricity Boards had connected many rural villages to 'the mains' for the first time, and electrical loads like this needed a good supply. As a result, many grain stores were either built new or housed in converted barns in the centre of villages. Unfortunately fans tend to be noisy, which would later upset neighbours. Where power was not available an old tractor or other engine might be used to drive the fan, while the waste heat from the tractor engine could be used to warm the air being drawn in.

Many farmers took up the grants that were offered to improve grain drying and storage facilities. Unlike in other countries, the British farmer was expected to store his grain and was not paid for it until it was sold, although prices were set to include a small payment for each week of storage. Just as when the grain had been stored in sheaves, the farmer did not get paid until long after harvest.

Built under licence to a Swedish design, the David Brown Albion was intended to replace the Albion Binder. PTO-driven, the Albion was introduced before tractors had a live power take-off. When a farmer recently tried an Albion behind a modern high-powered tractor with plenty of gears and a live PTO, he was impressed with how much higher an output was possible. The crop followed a direct route by conveyor into the drum, and the balloon tyres made it easy to tow.

Above: This Gleaner combine, part of the Midland Combines collection, was built by Allis Chalmers at Essendine in Lincolnshire. With the engine mounted high behind the grain tank, it was a layout less vulnerable to dust. As with the Massey Ferguson 780 alongside, air flow to the radiator was screened by a perforated mesh pillar. The returns elevator on the offside took oversize screenings back to the header platform, where they went right through the proper threshing process again. As well as reducing losses it meant that the operator could keep an eye on the return feed.

Below: The McCormick International B64 trailed harvester was built by International in Yorkshire. While it took some time to get into production, it represented a saving in dollars compared with importing similar machines from the United States.

Top and middle: The Claas Super Junior was a smaller version of the trailed Super. Cut material was conveyed to the drum by two rubberised canvas belts with the drum mounted lengthways. The bagging platform folded out over the nearside wheel.

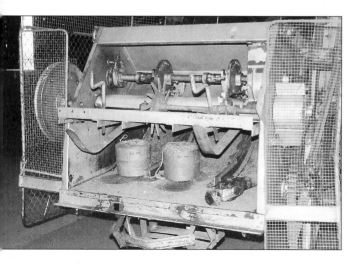

Left: A characteristic Claas fitting was the rear-mounted trusser, which tied off the threshed straw in neat bundles. This machine was stored for 20 years before being bought by Claas for its collection. The faded Red Star wrapper on the twine is a reminder of a familiar brand name of the past; it was made from sisal, much of which was grown in East Africa.

The design of these early stores would later impose a handicap on the use of combines. Any sort of grain-drying set-up that is fed by a reception arrangement will use some form of conveyor to move the grain to where it will be stored. With early combines it was also often felt worth putting the grain through some form of grain cleaner to remove impurities, such as small pieces of green weed. This often had the bonus of slightly reducing the effective moisture content. However, somewhere in the process there would be a bottleneck that would limit the rate at which grain could be taken in. If the farm's combine capacity was higher than this rate, some short-term arrangement would be needed to store the surplus. Such makeshift arrangements could involve double handling, and this build-up became particularly critical if there was any intention of carrying on through the night to beat the weather.

Many grain stores still in use today were first planned in the 1950s, and no designer could have anticipated the high output rates of today's combines. The combination of bottlenecks and complaints about noise meant that it sometimes made sense to build a completely new grain store elsewhere on the farm. This might be financed by selling the original buildings for conversion to up-market houses, and often their new owners would be loudest in complaining about the activities of farmers within 'their' village!

Many farms acquired their first pick-up baler during the 1950s. This simplified clearing the straw, although loading and stacking bales by hand was heavy work.

By the end of the 1950s most farmers had access to a combine. Binders were becoming increasingly uncommon apart from use on specialised crops like grass seeds. At the end of the 1940s a farm relying entirely on combines would have been seen as unusual. Ten years later a farm still using mainly binders would be regarded as just as unusual.

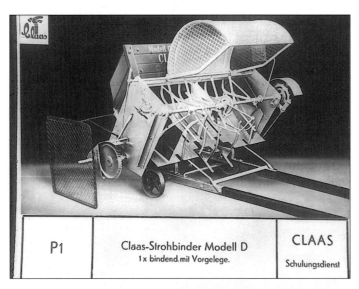

The Claas Model D trusser. The operating principle is similar to that of a binder, but with two securing bands of twine. The bundles produced are easy to handle either by hand or with a fork. *J. Mann*

This Claas harvest scene logo has lasted remarkably well.

6. DEALERS, AND DANGERS, THE 1960S

s farmers were offered a greater choice of new combines, more considered the reputation of the manufacturer and the local dealer. A good dealer held a comprehensive stock of spare parts — purchasing a combine was no use if a lack of back-up put it out of action. Moreover, a dealer with intelligent staff on call could do much to offset any shortcomings in a machine.

In turn, the dealers were helped by back-up from their suppliers. Certain importers earned particularly good reputations for their support of the machines they sold. Sometimes there were changes in the make of combine offered by a dealer, which could be due to factors outside his control. For example, when Massey Harris merged with Ferguson, many Fordson dealers were 'encouraged' to relinquish their Massey

combine agency, and instead they offered Ransomes. This company had a joint marketing arrangement with Ford at the time, and one sign of this was the uprated Fordson Major engine used to power the Ransome 902. Dealers could achieved success by getting an agency for a manufacturer that offered the dealership more potential.

In other cases, an importer might change supplier. The 'Bamford' name appeared on combines from BM Volvo of Sweden, Clayes of Belgium and Laverda from Italy, while Massey Ferguson combines have come from a variety of plants and suppliers at different times.

Even today, 1960s combines without cabs can still be found at work. This French-built International 8-41 was doing a good job in Wiltshire in 2000 despite being over 30 years old.

The tines on the reel have a feathering action like a paddle-steamer. When correctly set they drop into the crop and tend to prevent it falling forward as the cutter bar approaches.

Looking into the threshing drum below the registration number of the International 8-41. Access in order to clear blockages is particularly easy by removing a single cover. The auger shaft immediately above the drum is used to distribute oversized returns for rethreshing.

A close-up of the drum. The serrated beater bars do the actual rubbing as they pass close to the concave that wraps round the drum like a close-fitting mudguard.

Above: The grain is being discharged into a grain tank carried by a tipping trailer. Grain tanks often extended behind the body of a tipping trailer, giving a bigger volume of payload. The driver's disposable dust-mask keeps most of the dust out of his nose and throat. As the driver said, 'None of my neighbours can match my low depreciation costs!'

Middle: Weeks trailers came from Hessle, near Hull. By using pressed and formed steel the company produced lightweight and economical bodies to carry bulk grain. Being built up in panels, a third panel could be added for grass silage, or with a single panel they could carry roots or dung. Tandem axles were used to reduce the load on each tyre, and a grain chute has been added by the user to allow a controlled flow of grain into a hopper.

Right: After Clayson, Bamford, the well-respected machinery manufacturer of Uttoxeter, handled the BM Volvo combine for a while, deciding to import the well-known Volvo-owned Swedish Bolinders Munktell combines rather than manufacture its own. Volvo also purchased Arvika Termaenius, the maker of Viking combines. The Bamford agency was short-lived, as it then took on Laverda. This survivor is displayed at Midland Combines of Newark.

Left: Laverda combines were imported from Italy by Bamford for a period. Laverda was quick to adopt the detachable header idea; it hung on the two pegs on the elevator before being locked into position by the two screw clamps at the base. The cab is a later addition, and needed a home-made extension to provide access to all the driver's controls. With the header removed, the elevator that drags the crop into the threshing area can be seen.

Below: A closer view of the securing clamp. The hydraulic ram and spring are one of a pair that raise and lower the header. The spring can be used to support some of the header's weight, reducing the weight carried by the skids beneath. The dangling hydraulic pipes carry quick-release couplings; when connected to the header they raise and lower the reel and adjust its position.

Dania was one of Denmark's leading makers in 1966 when this machine was first imported into Britain. It is now preserved at Midland Combines of Newark.

Midland Shires Farmers demonstrated a good example of co-operation between dealer and importer. Each night during the harvest a vehicle was sent from Worcester to Mann's of Saxham. Farmers running Claas combines knew from experience that they could order spare parts as late as 8pm and start dismantling, and early next morning their parts would be available at the local branch. To the farmers and the dealer this trip was informally known as the 'Pony Express'. Mann's was willing to stay open all night to supply spare parts. Today this may not seem exceptional, but in the 1960s this level of service must have sold many Claas combines in the Worcestershire area.

Good staff were also important for a dealer, and news that a good man had left could strongly influence future sales. For many years they were referred to as 'mechanics', possessing an ability to get a machine running often using their own personal skill and tools. Later they became known as 'fitters', and it was alleged that repairs often consisted of fitting replacement parts. Today the same people are known as 'technicians', yet many of their tasks would

be familiar to an earlier mechanic. However, the introduction of sophisticated electronics and diagnostic tools has certainly made the job more technical.

Just as vital were the storemen. Harvesting has always been a stressful time, and any farmer faced with a broken-down combine would be even more stressed. A storeman's job often involved calming the customer enough to get more details of what exactly the problem was. Together they would pore over the appropriate thick spare parts book with its exploded drawings, their mutual aim being to identify the broken bit. Once identified, they could agree on its part number and record it. Part numbers overcame any language difficulties in the chain between factory and end user, and the storeman was only too well aware that getting one digit wrong would order entirely the wrong part.

At the same time fitters would be demanding parts urgently through another hatch. A paragon of a storeman would remain unflappable and helpful, but a bad storeman could lose customers rapidly.

Without good mechanics and storemen it was a struggle to make sales, and at harvest time the colour of the combines was evidence of the most successful local dealer.

Partly dismantled combines at Midland Combines of Newark provide users with a source of used spare parts. They also give us a chance to follow the route of the cut crop through a combine. As the crop leaves the cutter bar and header it is carried upwards by the chain-and-slat conveyor, which is arranged so that the flow continues whether the elevator housing is raised or lowered. Heavy object like stones tend to roll downhill into the stone trap.

At the top of the slope the straw is fed into the threshing drum, where it is whirled around and much of the grain is separated out, falling directly on to the sieves. Straw and some grain passes back for later separation.

An actual threshing drum removed from a combine. Its construction needs to be strong to resist the forces set up when threshing. The angled ribs impart a sideways movement as they pass over the screen, and separation comes from both the impact and the rubbing against the screen. The rasp bars, as they are called, are bolted for easy replacement; at the very least they were replaced as matched pairs. For best results it was recommended that the drum should always be removed and balanced if any alterations were made.

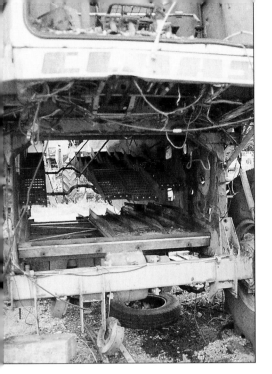

The straw moves on and up through the straw walkers (only three of the five are shown in position here). As the straw is vigorously shaken any grain drops through into channels at the bottoms of the walkers, whence it falls on to the sieves below; again they are only partly in place. The separated grain passes through the sieves, from where it is carried up to the grain tank for transport.

By their nature combines are particularly dangerous machines to operate. Like threshing machines before them, they are designed to treat straw vigorously. To do this large quantities of power are applied, mostly transmitted by a mixture of chains and belts. On an unprotected machine in operation, many of these belts would be capable of trapping clothing or even a limb, causing severe injury or perhaps death.

Some hazards were totally unexpected. Many early self-propelled machines had drive chains between the output shaft and the wheels. These were unprotected and tended to rust, and if one broke the driver had no transmission, no brakes and no way of stopping a runaway.

Until the 1960s the main regulations had dealt with guarding PTOs on trailer combines, and risk was accepted as a normal hazard of using machinery. It did have the effect of ensuring that operators remained alert, and relatively few were injured, considering the hazards.

To establish a better standard of guarding for all types of agricultural machinery, the Field Machinery Regulations were introduced. In the case of binders and combine harvesters these came into force in January 1965, threshing machines having been covered earlier, in 1960. Driving belts and chains with any sort of protruding fastener now had to be totally guarded; even smooth belts with no protruding fasteners had to be guarded at the point where the belt ran on to the pulley. A more general stipulation was that on any machine that carried an operator, all belts and chains must be guarded at every place where they would expose the worker to risk of injury.

Seats had to have an adequate back-rest or be shaped to hold the operator in place. The function of all levers had to be clearly marked. For the first time a novice operator could anticipate what would happen before the lever was operated.

The first effect of the arrival of these regulations was that existing machines had to be fitted with all sorts of modifications and bolted-on guards, which added to the frustration of any servicing or maintenance work. Moreover, designers and

Driver comfort in the mid-1960s consisted of two tubular steel arm-rests and easier adjustment of the driver's seat. Power steering and the spinner on the steering wheel allowed a driver to make quicker turns on the headland. By today's standards the two work lamps were not a lot of use, but flashing indicators added a touch of style. The fire extinguisher on the steps also seems rather inadequate.

manufacturers used the regulations to justify fitting far more elaborate guards on newly introduced machines. However, typically these were arranged on hinges or mountings so that they could be swung out of the way for service work, and after the aggravations of dealing with makeshift guards, these new ones represented a vast improvement. Adequate ladders also had to be provided to gain access to the machines. Many designers used the guards as part of the styling for new models, and since they offered what was a protective cover over much of the machine, they reduced the need for a waterproof sheet, which had been a vital part of the equipment for an early combine. Every night the machine had been carefully covered to keep off the rain and dew,

continuing what had been the practice with threshing machines. The new guards also protected greasing points from dust, making greasing a cleaner job. This was aided by a tendency to use self-lubricated bearings that did not require a daily greasing.

As we have already seen, to ease the driver's work many manufacturers were gradually introducing hydraulic assistance for various tasks, such as raising and lowering the cutter bar, adjusting the variable belt drive for forward speed, and later, power assistance for the steering and braking.

By the end of the 1960s combines had evolved from a tangle of belts and chains to a more styled look, and while their appearance was redesigned, the opportunity was also taken to increase their output.

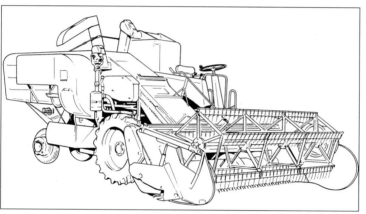

Left: The Massey Ferguson 788 was a restyled version of the 780. The most noticeable external changes were the horizontal cooling air intake for the radiator and the reverse slope of the straw hood. Safety legislation meant better steps for the driver, while the swing-away auger reduced the space needed when the combine was parked for the winter or travelling in narrow lanes.

Below: Not every grower needs a new machine. For smaller growers an older combine can still deal with their crops at modest cost. Since 1990 this Massey Harris 788 has been giving good service in West Wales. Despite being over 40 years old there is no reason why this should not continue with reasonable maintenance. *D. O. Jones*

Underneath the operator's platform of a Clayson is the power steering control and the hydraulic master cylinders linked to the brake pedals. Many of the components used were common to other motor vehicles of the time. The black patch was for sealing silage bags, but here it has been used by an ingenious driver to reduce the risk of chafing. The build-up of dust and rubbish shows how unpleasant repairs in the field could be — imagine that itchy dust falling on you as you worked!

When they were announced, the Massey Ferguson 400 and 500 combines marked the start of a completely new look. For the first time they were styled. The engine was moved up high out of the dust, the grain tank extended across the width of the machine, and extensive guards hid many of the working parts. The main external differences, apart from badging, were that the 500 had a bigger operator's platform, the steps were behind the wheel, and the drive wheels were larger than specified for the 400.

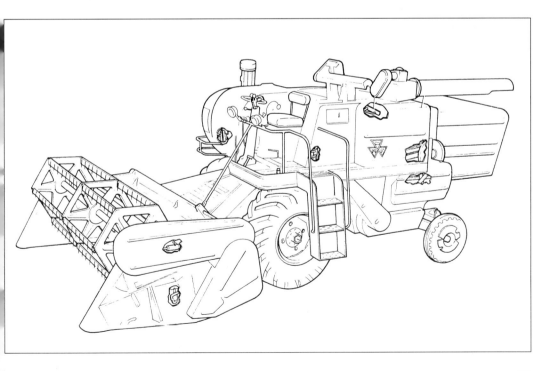

Top: With the launch of the 400 and 500 series Massey Ferguson came up with a simple-to-use idea for the discharge auger. By pivoting it at a point above the grain tank, it could be stowed over the top of the machine out of harm's way. According to specification it could be swung either manually or by hydraulic operation. By mounting a light inboard it was possible for the operator to focus it to illuminate the discharge.

Middle: With the engine and header removed, the layout of this Massey Ferguson 515 is more clearly seen. The sturdy front axle supports the main structure with the threshing drum immediately above. The engine is mounted above, with the operator sitting to the left-hand side. Much of the upper area is occupied by the substantial grain tank behind the engine bay.

Left: The actual front drive axle seen from behind. The belt pulley on the left is driven at a variable speed under the influence of an expanding pulley. The clutch on the right of the gearbox isolates it for gear changes and moving off. The gearbox also includes the differential, with the drive coming out as a pair of shafts (the left one is hidden) to the disc brakes and final reduction gearbox on each wheel. This compact and effective drive arrangement was used by Massey Ferguson.

7. MONITORING PROGRESS, THE 1970s

During the 1970s a new crop became increasingly popular — oil-seed rape. This is the crop that produces expanses of bright yellow flowers in the countryside. It is actually related to the cabbage family, Brassica, but produces its seed in small pods. When crushed or treated with a solvent, the seeds release rape oil. This was originally used to lubricate steam engines, but later it was found to be edible and is used in the manufacture of margarine or further refined to make cooking oil or salad cream. It was widely promoted as an alternative to a cereal crop with the aim of reducing European oil-seed imports. Additionally, it has been technically demonstrated that diesel engines will run on rape oil; the exhaust smells rather like a fish and chip shop extractor fan, but the fumes are more acceptable in city traffic than those of a conventional diesel engine.

Harvesting rape presents a number of special challenges. As it grows it forms a tangled mass, which is too clinging for conventional dividers to cope with. Usually a vertical knife is mounted on one end of the cutter bar to cut the tangled mass cleanly; this can be driven electrically or hydraulically, and is usually fitted as an accessory in a kit that sometimes includes an additional hydraulic pump to be installed elsewhere on the combine.

The first rape varieties used to ripen unevenly, so to overcome this the crop would be cut and left in neat rows to weather and ripen before being picked up by a special attachment on the combine. This had to be done very gently to prevent the ripe pods shattering and losing their seed on the ground.

After some false starts it was found that machines intended for cutting peas would do a reasonable job of cutting and swathing rape. Specialised swathing machines based on designs used in the United States were imported. These would normally be operated by

The driver of this Massey Ferguson 36 on the top of the Cotswolds in Oxfordshire is direct-cutting rape without any modifications to the header at all. The rear-mounted chopper is fragmenting the rape straw, making it easy to plough in. While this does absorb engine power, it gets two jobs done at once.

Above: Oil-seed rape is sometimes cut into swathes to allow it to dry. By leaving a long stubble the driver can undercut it. The swathe forms such a tangled mass that it is pulled into the feeder without needing any help from the reel. Rape seed is so small that even short lengths of rape straw cannot pass through the small sieves needed for this crop.

Below: As rape tangles while it grows, cutting it becomes a challenge. While the normal cutter bar makes a good job of undercutting the crop, the tangles mean a cut crop is constantly trying to drag in the adjoining crop, leading to jams. One solution was this vertical knife used to part the tangles by cutting through them. This eliminates tangles with the reel yet when in the cutting position it is clear of the ground. This conversion was made by Shelbourne Reynolds, which would later produce the stripper header.

contractors and had a very short working season. However, over the last few years plant breeders have bred more uniform varieties that can be harvested direct with a suitable combine.

The seeds of oil-seed rape are in the form of small black spheres. In bulk they flow like water, thus doing an excellent job of finding the smallest leaks either in the combine or the transport. Indeed, many operators find it worth sealing potential leaks with duct tape before starting on this crop. The setting of the reel is also critical to prevent pods shattering before they have fallen on to the header table, and the air blast over the sieves has to be cut to prevent the seeds being blown out of the back like weed seeds. The forward speed has to be kept down for gentle harvesting and to avoid getting a tangled mass wrapped around the reel. With lower yields than other cereal crops, the grain tank takes longer to fill.

With so many snags, why do farmers continue to grow rape? It can be a cheap crop to establish, and can usually be harvested before other crops are ready. Rape can also be grown for industrial purposes on land where growing cereals would not be permitted under set-aside regulations, and its different requirements mean that it can be used as a break from continuous cereals.

During the decade, with most farms having access to a combine, demand started to tail off. Ransome recognised that its designs were being outclassed, but rather than develop a new model it withdrew from the market, and instead bought Catchpole, the maker of sugar beet harvesters, in effect replacing combines with more specialised sugar beet harvesters.

Another blue combine was the remarkable Lely Victory, built in Wiltshire. Disconnecting some catches, the two halves of the cutter bar and reel could be folded. Here for the first time was a machine with a wide cut that could travel legally on the road without the need to notify the police. British Lely was a successor to Fisher Humphries, so again a combine maker had a threshing machine background.

Bigger combines meant that grain was coming in too fast for many smaller dryers to cope. A popular new way of storage was in large heaps on the floor held in by retaining walls; however, one or two users underestimated the thrust exerted by the heaped grain and had walls collapse. By running ducts under the floor or even on the floor, air can be blown through the grain while stored, which can both dry the grain and lower its temperature. Fan size will limit the drying potential, but as long as the fans are kept running, a floor store can probably take in grain as fast as it is combined, effectively removing the bottleneck caused by grain dryers. For very moist grain it may be necessary to turn it later to ensure the drying is more even.

Lely of Wootton Bassett, Wiltshire, was the successor to Fisher Humphries, and its Victory combine featured a unique design of folding header either 4.2 or 5.4 metres wide. As it could fold without being detached, it proved particularly useful for contractors. Lely was also an early pioneer of hydrostatic transmission. Until detachable headers became more popular few combines could match the output of a Victory.

Making the headers detachable reduced the space needed when parking or storing a combine in a building. On the left of this Claas Senator is the vertical elevator bringing the grain up into the tank behind the driver. To hold the rear down when a heavy header was fitted, a box was provided at the back to be filled with sand or soil as ballast, although using sand from a beach could cause unexpected corrosion from the salt content.

Above: The discharge spout from the grain tank was always vulnerable to damage from overhanging branches. By making it fold back, Clayes reduced the overall width of a 1545 and minimised this risk of damage.

Above: A redesign provided a mounting that allowed the discharge spout to swing out and up. This also reduced the risk of grain spillage when the discharge auger was disconnected.

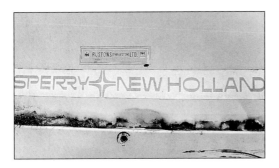

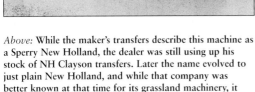

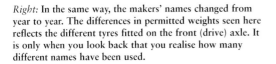

Above: While the maker's transfers describe this machine as a Sperry New Holland, the dealer was still using up his stock of NH Clayson transfers. Later the name evolved to just plain New Holland, and while that company was better known at that time for its grassland machinery, it was felt helpful to drop the Claeys and Clayson names.

Right: In the same way, the makers' names changed from year to year. The differences in permitted weights seen here reflects the different tyres fitted on the front (drive) axle. It is only when you look back that you realise how many different names have been used.

Above: The Massey Ferguson 487 was first built in Germany, but production was later transferred to France. The auger could be folded, and as the operator's platform projected much further there was no need for any recess to accommodate it.

Below: The styling and layout of the 487 followed that of the earlier 500. This drawing is taken from a spare parts list, which was a vital accompaniment to each combine. Each number led the operator to a more detailed illustration on which each component had its own unique number. Quoting this number meant that parts could be ordered even when the operator, the mechanic, the importer and the factory personnel all spoke different languages.

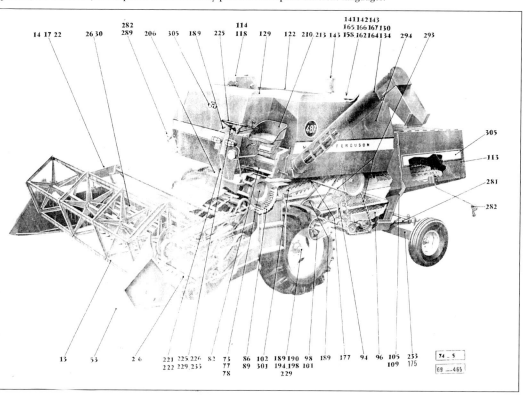

Left: Adding the Fiat name signified that the company had recently acquired control of Laverda. This backing helped with the marketing of Laverda combines in many territories.

Below left: Small Claas combines are less common, but they did meet one specialised requirement. Many agricultural trials and experiments involve growing plots of different varieties or treatments in the hope that their worth will be measured by variations in yields. Harvesting individual plots with a small combine makes it easier to assess the yield from each separate plot. This is a bagger example, where the platform and guard rail can be easily folded in to reduce the travelling width.

Right: Outdoor silos like these by Ideal are filled from the top by a spiral auger elevator, often also made by Ideal. The construction is of corrugated iron, and being circular, the forces exerted by the grain are resisted by the circles of iron in tension. While they may appear flimsy when empty, they are much stronger when filled. Perhaps appropriately, Ideal shared an office building with the Spirella Corset Company in Oxford Street, London! The tractor-driven fan is blowing drying air into the base.

Below: This GT mobile grain dryer was supplied by Opico. Using propane gas, mobile dryers offered a grain-drying set-up that could be easily moved to different locations. To a tenant farmer this offered a satisfactory method of drying grain that could be sold if he left the farm.

Above: For drivers who mislaid instruction books, Claas had an effective answer. Essential advice was given in six languages, including the cheerful warning that if the brakes were too strongly applied the combine might tip over! This would be more of a problem on steep gradients allied with high speed.

Below: When changing the variety or type of grain it is important to clean the combine to prevent cross-contamination, especially if there is a chance of a crop being used for seed. Inspection flaps make is easier to clean out grain elevators, and can also give access in order to clear blockages. The actual transport is by rubber flaps attached to a roller chain; the flap material is a laminated rubber and textile construction, like that of a tyre, and in the event of a blockage it will bend rather than break.

Another trend was to give the combine driver better information about what was happening, supplementing the information he was picking up with his senses. The latter might include unfamiliar noises suggesting problems with a belt or bearing, while slip clutches were intended to make an unpleasant noise if overloaded. Smell might warn of a slipping belt, fire or overheating. Vibration might indicate an unbalanced drum or a potential jam, while eyes looked out for problems in front of the cutter bar, the state of the crop and how well the reel was bringing in the crop to the knife. Feel could be used to judge the quality of a sample grabbed from the tank, or the humidity of the atmosphere. Getting off the combine and rummaging in the harvested swathe might provide clues as to how efficiently the combine was doing its job. The most important sense of all was, as it still is, common sense.

While all this information was being gathered, the operator had to judge whether to ignore it or act on it, a balancing act between pressing on regardless and spending so long getting the adjustments and settings exactly right that it was raining by the time the combine was running to his entire satisfaction.

The faster a combine travels in a field the more crop it can cut and harvest, but as speed increases the threshing and separating mechanism will become overloaded, and not all the grain will be separated from the straw, some passing out of the back of the combine. Once this was noticed by the farmer the combine driver would be told off and would slow down to be on the safe side. In practice it meant that most combines were driven more cautiously than necessary.

Bill Reed and his colleagues at the University of Saskatchewan in Canada developed the Grain Loss Monitor, their aim being to measure if any grain was going to waste. While trying various ideas, their farming background came up with the answer. Locally most combines were fitted with spinning straw spreaders, and driving up close in a pick-up truck odd grains in the straw might hit the truck with a characteristic 'ping'. You can hear something similar if you get too close to a gritter spreading sand or salt on the road. The new monitors measured the 'ping' of grain going to waste, and once set, while there was no waste, the driver knew that he could safely go faster. As Bill put it, the monitor did the same job as the boss of a threshing machine, urging on output but constantly checking that no grain was going to waste. Sometimes modest losses were tolerated if the combine could achieve even greater output, but that was a matter of judgement between the farmer and the driver.

The Smith Roles company of Saskatoon, Saskatchewan, was the first to manufacture grain loss monitors. They were spotted and imported into the UK by Ewart Chapman, who had a particular interest in applying electronics to agriculture. Later his business was acquired by Rural Development Services, which had previously specialised in cheap farm buildings. Their promotion made their version of grain loss monitors accepted as a useful guide, and they were claimed to increase the work rate of most combines.

Meanwhile, manufacturers not yet ready to offer grain loss monitoring went to great lengths to explain how insignificant these losses were in relation to the combine's throughput. Even today combines can leave prominent green stripes in the field, although comparatively little grain is needed to produce such a stripe, much of which may well have resulted from the germination of shrivelled and undersized grains anyway. Today grain loss monitoring is so widely accepted as an aid to combine driving that most manufacturers offer their own version.

Other indicators were introduced to warn of straw building up internally. Typically this would be a roof-

Right: While casting doubt on the need for them, manufacturers were busy developing their own versions of the Grain Loss Monitor. In this example, mounted on the back of the sieves, bulky material like straw is carried over the top by the seven fingers, while light material will be blown clear by the air blast through the sieves. Any grain going to waste will fall through the fingers and hit the microphone underneath. Each grain striking the microphone sends a characteristic signal along the wire to the meter, where readings warn the driver if losses are becoming unacceptable. Robust construction was needed as the monitors got a constant vigorous shaking mounted on the reciprocating sieves.

Below: Clayes favoured sitting the driver centrally and over the elevator. With the engine up high, the drum could go over the front wheels, leaving plenty of room for straw separation and grain treatment. After the straw goes through the drum it meets another smaller spinning cylinder that directs it to a tined drum that rubs it over a second concave before fluffing up the straw well, prior to its falling on to the walkers, the intention being to improve the separation of the grain from the straw.

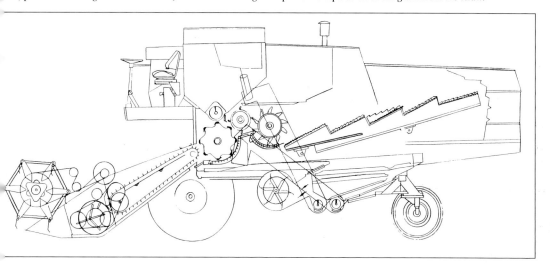

mounted flap that closed a switch when lifted by too much straw. Shaft rotation monitors detected a shaft slowing down, which could be the first symptom of a slipping belt or clutch. The output from these various monitors and switches was presented as light and sound signals from which the driver was able to get even more information.

One problem that arose from combining in bulk rather than by the sackful was judging the yield of grain from a field, and various attempts were made to overcome this. Most early attempts focused on weighing the grain as it passed through a fixed point in the grain store, but often this became the bottleneck that limited the throughput of grain.

Left: Yields of grain are checked with the Weylode gauge shown by the cab. This measures the pressure needed to slightly tip a trailer, and thus how much weight there is in the trailer. Even so-called full loads can vary in weight according to variety of grain and soil type.

Below: On smaller farms the combine driver may have to cart the corn as well. Lack of transport has halted this Claas Senator — the two circular windows show a full grain tank, so no more can be done until it is emptied. However, using a second-hand combine that is actually too big for a farm's needs means that the harvest can be gathered in quickly when conditions are right.

One simple approach was the Weylode, which measured the weight of loads by assessing the oil pressure needed to support a slightly tipped trailer-load of grain; this system is still widely used after 30 years. Other designers felt that yield recording should take place on the combine, and various manufacturers introduced weighing equipment either working on the grain as it entered the tank or measuring the contents discharged from the tank into the trailer.

Most trailers left the factory with little more than token brakes, and on most they were difficult to operate from the driving seat. As a result, most emergency stops were still achieved with only the tractor brakes working on the tractor's rear axle, which could result in a jack-knife under unfavourable conditions. However, few tractors could exceed 15mph in gear, so serious accidents were fairly rare, although most drivers would admit to having frightened themselves at least once.

Right: As combines have grown in size and output, bigger trailers have become necessary. Welded sides reduce the risk of leaks and tandem axles keep the load on individual tyres acceptable. To get as much as possible in each load the trailer has stopped and the combine driver is moving the combine to position the flow of grain.

Below: Without a tractor driver to collect grain by running alongside the combine, one alternative is to park empty trailers on the headland. The combine does have to stop and unload, but at least combining can continue. The two nearest trailers are both made by Weeks of Hull with a payload of around 4 tonnes. The tandem-axle trailer with the tractor can carry as much as both the other two.

Hauling grain on the road highlighted the advantages of the tractor foot throttle when it was introduced for snappier gear changes, and various firms began to offer systems that would apply the trailer brakes from the driver's seat. Oil pressure to apply brakes, oil pressure to hold brakes off against a powerful spring, and compressed air operation all had their supporters. Germany favoured compressed air braking, while France used hydraulic pressure trapped in an accumulator. The system eventually adopted in Britain used a special hydraulic valve to produce hydraulic pressure at a tapping. This pressure was proportional to the force of the driver's foot on the brake pedal.

Flashing indicators and tail-lights also started to appear on trailers, and gradually tractor-trailer outfits became better equipped to mingle with traffic on rural roads.

One big obstacle to acquiring a combine was paying for it — such a major capital outlay has often been beyond the reach of all but the biggest farms. Using a contractor was a way of getting the use of a combine without having to buy one, but many combines were purchased with the aid of bank loans or hire purchase. Around 1970 it was realised that if the combine was purchased on lease, the company actually owning it could still claim capital allowances against tax. As a result, they could accept what appeared to be attractively low repayments each year, and many sophisticated purchasers adopted this

arrangement. The one snag was that at the end of a leasing arrangement it was not possible legally to purchase the combine outright, although many machinery dealers devised some way to achieve the same result. A few specialist companies started to offer a combine hire service, whereby the farmer would pay an agreed sum for the exclusive use of a combine for one year.

The result of these somewhat complex financial arrangements was that farmers were often able to acquire a more sophisticated and expensive combine than they thought they could afford, which made good sense especially if the new combine could replace two smaller machines. Moreover, when grain prices fell later on they had relatively modern machinery and could manage without replacing it for some years.

Optional cabs began to be offered, protecting the driver from much of the dust and chaff in the atmosphere and providing a significant improvement in working conditions. Not so acceptable was that trapped heat from the glass in the cab made temperatures excessive. Cooling for the cab was needed, and the first coolers relied on some form of water evaporation to cool the air drawn into the cab.

These German-built John Deeres are awaiting new owners at a well-known combine dealer. Built by the former Lanz company, taken over by Deere, they show off the familiar green livery with the 'leaping deer' logo on the back.

Right: An after-market cab fitted to a mid-1980s Claas Dominator 85. The Mann's logo was used by the British importers at that time; for a short time Mann's was associated with Howard Rotavator. Before air-conditioning, a driver would have been grateful for the relief on a hot day provided by this combine's Comfort King cab cooler from Great Plains Industries of Wichita, Kansas. The cooler is housed in the roof and includes two dry and two wet filters to ensure that the driver enjoys a cool and dust-free atmosphere. The maker claimed that the cooler absorbed only ¼hp instead of the 5hp needed for equivalent air-conditioning.

Below: A close-up of the cooler. If the air blown into the cab passes through a moist filter, some moisture will evaporate, appreciably cooling the air stream. With the air passing through two dry filters and two moist filters, it is both cooled and cleaned before entering the cab.

Below: A Deutz Fahr 1202 with an optional cab makes a good job of a clean barley crop in Wiltshire. This machine has a particularly smooth-running knife drive; by reducing vibration as the crop is being cut, it was claimed that less grain was shaken out of the heads and lost before they were cut.

Above: The horse plough of 100 years ago would have been totally unable to bury the amount of straw left by even a small combine today.

Left: If the straw left by a combine is not cleared from the field it can make ploughing difficult. Plough-makers are building ploughs with much more clearance between each body, which reduces the chance of straw building up and causing a blockage.

Below: Most ploughs today are reversible — the driver can make them plough left or right as required. This allows a field to be ploughed without leaving any ridges or furrows, and the resulting level surface makes for a much smoother ride for the combine driver with less risk of a wide header digging into the ground. Conversely, heavy combines and loaded grain trailers can pack the ground hard, especially in wet conditions, making the ploughing tractor work harder.

Above: Where the straw left by the combine was to be collected, it used to be a heavy job. The pick-up baler helped, but clearing the bales was tiring work in the sun. By towing a bale sledge they could at least be collected into regular-sized stacks.

Below: With the correct grab on the front-end loader, a tractor driver could pick up eight bales at a time and stack them on a trailer without leaving the tractor seat. Unloading and much of the stacking could be done in the same way — another exhausting job made much easier.

The driver's job was thus becoming more comfortable while the combines were getting more complicated. Still the objective was to allow one driver to harvest more grain in an hour's work. However, these bigger combines were leaving more straw in the fields to be cleared, and where there was little demand for it some farmers favoured burning it where it lay. The resulting fires looked spectacular but killed many weed seeds; glider pilots welcomed the thermals they generated, conservationists claimed that they damaged hedges, while drifting smoke could cause accidents. Some users favoured choppers on combines to make it easier to work the straw back into the soil, but most were looking for more efficient ways of clearing the straw behind the combine. The arrival of the Bigbaler,

As combines got bigger and took wider cuts they left swathes of straw that were getting too big for conventional balers. Two Gloucestershire farmers designed the Howard Bigbaler, and by producing fewer and bigger bales they had a machine that could match the output of the biggest combines. While today's big bales are similar in weight, the bales are much more dense.

and later big round balers, offered the answer. For farmers who preferred small bales, methods of mechanically loading them appeared.

By the end of the 1970s the driver had more information, more power assistance and more stylish machines, while clearing the straw could be a less laborious job.

8. Greater Sophistication, the 1980s

As we enter the 1980s this account ceases to be a history. Despite their age, most combines manufactured from now on will still have been in use as the 21st century dawned.

A new expression, 'combinable crops', came into use to cover crops that were commonly harvested with a combine harvester. In practical terms this referred to wheat, barley and oats, as well as oil-seed rape, sunflowers, lupins and linseed.

A combine harvester was becoming an expensive and sophisticated machine to buy, and a skilful driver was needed to get the best output from such a complicated machine. Many farms that could use a combine were handicapped by lack of both funds and a skilled operator, and some farmers started to explore alternative way of getting the crops combined.

It became much less common to see a new combine supplied without some form of cab. Air-conditioning

Below: Burning straw in a Dutch barn can even heat and often rolled steel joists, allowing the frame to distort and sag until it cools again. No wonder farmers appear over-fussy about fire precautions.

Below right: Fire is always a threat when using a combine. It appears from the damage to this John Deere 1075 that the fire started in the engine bay and was

probably extinguished fairly quickly. A burning combine in the middle of a field of straw can soon get out of control.

Bottom: Until it was finally prohibited by regulations, setting fire to straw was a quick and effective way of preparing a field for the next crop. Done correctly there was little risk of the blaze getting out of control. *Ray Bird*

Above: Overheating has always been a problem with combine engines, and the usual cause is the radiator clogging with dust and chaff. However big the filters fitted to prevent this, they can still block. Rotary filters have an internal rotating arrangement that blocks part of the filter while brushing out any rubbish attached. Most of this rubbish drops clear, leaving plenty of clear filter to admit cooling air. Cleaning radiators or filters was a job most drivers were happy to see the back of.

Below: A cab was becoming a very desirable accessory for a combine driver, and various makers offered them as add-on accessories. While the expanse of glass made them exceedingly warm on a sunny day, sealing and filters kept out much of the troublesome dust. A cab also kept rain and dew off the seat and instruments when parked.

Above: A spectacular feature of the New Holland Clayson 8000 range was its all-glass cab. Three large sheets of tinted glass were literally stuck together to make a cab with no blind spots, while the forward slope of the windscreen reduced the chance of reflections. Hanging from the lower offside mirror brackets are two crop lifters; fitted to the cutter bar, they are used to lift flattened crops enough to be cut.

Right: This simple form of shaft monitor works by measuring the changes in magnetic field as each tooth passes a sensor. This fairly robust arrangement feeds a signal up the wire to the instrument panel. An unexpected change in the signal carried could be a driver's first warning of an impending blockage.

was the only real answer to heat build-up, and at the same time sound insulation was specified to reduce in-cab noise. A fitted stereo radio ensured more acceptable background noise. All this meant that the driver was becoming isolated from unusual sounds, which are often the first clue to an impending breakdown. Now the first warning was more likely to come from a flashing light in the cab, so additional monitoring equipment was going to be needed to help the driver in his new circumstances.

It may be recalled that early combines had deprived rats and mice of winter accommodation in stacks.

Now modern monitoring equipment offered them a chance of revenge. If a combine harvester is not thoroughly cleaned at the end of the year it can provide them with shelter — it may be far less insulated than a straw stack, but they can survive. And as a change from grain and weed seeds, the rodents enjoy nibbling plastic-coated wires. This may seem a minor nuisance, but when the combine is started for the new season these wires will short out, which can cause serious damage to modern electronics. Reinforced wire and better protection can overcome the problem, which was not spotted for the first few years; typically a new combine would have been carefully looked after during those first years, and with all the grain cleaned out it would have been of little interest to passing rodents. Often it is the second or even third owner who is less scrupulous about keeping the combine clean over winter. Really it is only another example of nature finding a way to fight back against modern developments!

For operators without a cab the defence company Racal offered an alternative. The Airstream Helmet was a fibreglass safety helmet complete with a transparent visor that totally covered the head. A small battery-operated fan blew filtered air into the helmet, and the slight pressure generated kept dust out of the mask, allowing the wearer to breathe clean air. Although they worked well, wearers did feel slightly self-conscious.

Power steering and sometimes power brakes started to feature in most specifications. Light steering mean one-hand steering, with the other hand free for controls

Ignoring all other factors, the wider the cut a combine could make, the greater the area of ground pe

While the driver may look like a spaceman, he is enjoying a supply of dust-free air to breathe. He is wearing an Airstream Helmet, which includes a small battery pack to power a fan. As this slightly pressurises the area under the helmet, dust is kept out. As a bonus, the transparent visor keeps the dust out of his eyes. The trailer is a Weeks with grain sides built up from two panels. It is fitted with an Idleback, a small gap at the base of th back that allows grain to flow under it, where it is trapped by the substantial protruding lip. When the trailer is tipped to discharge its load the grain flows out without any need for the tractor driver to release any catch.

'Tramlines' in a crop make it possible to apply fertilizer and sprays much later in the growing season, resulting in heavier crops for combines to tackle, but with far fewer weeds.

hour that could be covered at a given forward speed. Not surprisingly, the demand was therefore for machines with a greater width of cut, which made them wider when travelling on the road. When servicing or repairing a combine it had always been possible to remove the header mechanism after some dismantling, but designers realised that if this process was made easier and quicker, the width for travelling could be reduced. If the header could be carried separately on a suitable trailer it could either be hitched to the combine or otherwise towed between jobs. The designers probably recalled how binders were transported. Other advantages were that a much higher-output combine could be stored in the same size building. The reduced width of the main machine made transport by road much easier, even though the dimensions still fell outside normally permitted load widths.

If a combine was being pushed for the highest output there was always the risk of choking it with too much straw. Extra clutches meant that the header could be stopped while the drum continued, allowing the best chance of the machine clearing itself. Clearing a jammed header could be a tiring job, but fitting an auxiliary reverse drive and clutch allowed the operator to reverse the header to discharge the jam back on to the ground. With luck, on the second attempt it would be swallowed and threshed. Under these circumstances operators appreciated not having to leave their seat.

By now makers were giving much more attention to the needs and preferences of operators. Declining numbers of farm employees meant that many combine operators were now closely related to the person signing the cheques and making the buying

Right: The cab on this Claas Dominator 86 is much better integrated into the styling of the rest of the machine. With the header detached and the auger neatly stowed, an 86 could be driven on the road with only an escort and without the need to notify the police. The ECF logo is that of the Eastern Counties Farmers co-operative in East Anglia.

Below: To avoid picking up the threshed straw on the ground, the driver has lifted the cutter bar of this John Deere 975 as it comes out of the crop. If this was not done the cutter bar would harvest the straw again; some would be chopped into short lengths, which could behave like grain on the sieves and spoil the sample produced.

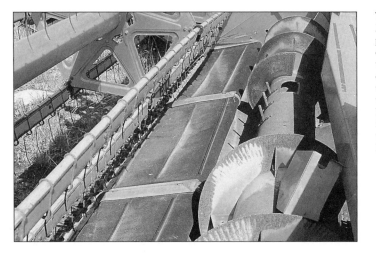

The Powerflow design of header from Massey Ferguson's Canadian combine plant had these rubberised conveyors carrying the cut crop back until it was within reach of the auger. It was claimed that the bigger gap between the reel and the auger meant that there was less chance of a blockage on the header. The aim was to speed up the feed rate into the conveyor to the threshing area while reducing grain losses caused by the reel.

decisions, and this allowed them to put the operator's point of view forcibly.

Variable-belt transmissions were becoming hard pressed to transmit all the power available from the bigger engines, and as combines got heavier considerable power was needed to move them along on hills or soft going. For larger combines, makers started to offer the option of hydrostatic transmission; the engine drove a large hydraulic pump, which delivered oil under pressure to one or two hydraulic motors coupled to the drive wheels. The output of the pump could be varied by a simple control, and even though the pump was driven at a constant speed this made it easy for the operator to adjust the forward speed. On some transmissions a movement of the same lever could reverse the output of the pump. Operators thus enjoyed precise control with minimal effort.

The Ford Motor Company acquired New Holland from the Sperry Rand Corporation, and at first the Ford and New Holland names were both retained. However, after restructuring, the business became Ford New Holland, and as a result most Ford tractor dealers changed to selling New Holland combines.

Most manufacturers started to increase the number of models offered. Distinctions between models would include the size and make of engine specified, with perhaps a choice of sieve and straw walker sizes. In turn this might affect the widths of the headers on offer. Extra engine power might be useful if a straw chopper was fitted or for hilly ground, and fitting a turbocharged version of an engine addressed this. By combining these features a range of models with different names or type numbers could be produced without requiring too many different components.

Being a new model range, mechanics needed to be trained in the correct way to service the Sperry New Holland 8000. At the end of each course a certificate would be awarded, which was often displayed in the dealer's premises. *Author's collection*

Combines were getting more sophisticated, and most are still in use many years later.

Within Europe during the late 1980s it was recognised that European grain production was outstripping demand. You might think that this would be welcomed as a chance to relieve world hunger, but instead it was proposed that farmers be prohibited from growing so large an area of grain. Various schemes have been operated. To the onlooker fields that could be growing grain appear to be neglected and growing only weeds and rubbish, and most farmers regard this as shameful. Politicians justify it as Europe's Common Agricultural Policy (CAP). At first under CAP, grain prices had remained acceptable, but now prices were starting to drop.

These changes affected demand for combines in several ways. Some farmers elected to stop growing grain crops altogether, in effect retiring but keeping the farm. Others argued that the reduction in the area grown relieved the pressure on their combine so that replacement could be delayed.

Above: **John Deere offered the 1174 SII with hydrostatic transmission, which gave the driver an infinitely variable selection of forward speeds. Used effectively, it made for greater flexibility and higher output.**

Below: **In operation the Clayson 8070 requires some engine power, but the 140hp Ford engine can cope. A straw chopper is fitted, although stowed out of use; chopped and spread straw could be ploughed in to save work during the harvest.**

In the past, fields might be down to grass for some years before being ploughed again for cropping. As part of the CAP only those fields that were currently growing crops were eligible to continue to grow them. A few astute farmers identified that it was permissible not to grow grain on the headlands, producing fields with what appeared to be a wide unsown area around the edge. These unsown headlands made turning the combine easier and saved the job of harvesting the later-ripening grain in the shade of hedges.

Above: With 15 years of good service completed, this John Deere is still pushing on in Wiltshire in its personal dust cloud. The odd plants sticking up are wild oats. Hanging on the rear ladder are the lifters which fit on the cutterbar to help deal with a flattened crop.

Below: The 8050 fitted about midway in the six-model Clayson range. With a 116hp Ford engine it could handle headers up to 13 feet wide. While all of Clayson's 8000 series shared the same drum and cab, variations of engine, transmission and separating area gave each model a distinct character. For example, the 8070 had a bigger Ford engine, but the two models were identical in external size. Despite this, at just over 8 tonnes the 8070 weighed a tonne more.

Above: A bigger drum is the starting point for building a higher-output combine, and solid construction is needed to prevent any risk of distortion, always a risk with a massive assembly spinning at over 1,000rpm. Rather like a car wheel, combine drums have to be accurately balanced for weight distribution. With the drum removed from the combine, the rasp bars can be seen more clearly; the grooves alternate in direction to give a rubbing action but preventing any build-up of straw moving in one direction.

Below: Laverda earned a reputation for robust construction and modest repair costs. The access ladder can be swung out of the way when not needed. The missing lower side guard is a single panel, which, when opened or removed, gives excellent access to components.

The Fortschritt 514 was manufactured in East Germany before reunification, and gained a reputation as a high-output machine at a relatively modest price. As the elevator chain has been removed, the drive sprockets can be seen. Above the grain tank are modifications to increase tank capacity, while the wire ropes from the top of the grain tank are to support the auger.

The Fortschritt still used this folding auger arrangement, which, like the early Clayson design, could be unlatched and swung through 90 degrees to fit in a recess along the side of the body. As this involved disconnecting the outlet it was done only when travelling between jobs or for storage. Low first cost made such shortcomings tolerable.

Combines had ever-longer working lives and, even when they were left outside, better paint finishes and large guards offered good weather protection. After over 20 years the paintwork on this Massey Ferguson 506 is still respectable. The operator's ladder is loose on the elevator and the unloading auger is missing. The chain-and-slat elevator at the front carries the crop up to the threshing drum.

9. CONSOLIDATION,
THE 1990s AND TODAY

On the modern farm sprays control most weeds and pests, new conservation techniques can reduce the impact of low rainfall, and plant breeders have developed new varieties promising better yields. As we have seen, machinery manufacturers have done much to speed the harvest, and demand for grain has risen throughout the world.

Yet despite these huge advances farmers still have problems. A grain crop still takes a full year to complete a growing cycle, and only then is it fit to be harvested. By contrast, supermarkets or factories can raise profits by reducing the delay between buying in raw materials and selling their products to the customer. With the chance of more production cycles each year, they can justify expensive machinery, which they can use to earn income or reduce costs all year round. Combines always spend far longer parked up each year than harvesting.

Farmers are well used to living with the farming year. But a far more difficult hazard frustrates their plans — politicians! Since the majority of votes are to be obtained from town-dwellers, this is where they direct their priorities. Politicians will always vote in favour of keeping down the cost of food to the consumer, and to cereal growers this shows itself as an urge to direct and control farm output.

European co-operation was first described as the Common Market, and the stated aim was to unify policies between countries. Alarmed by reports of 'Grain Mountains' during the late 1980s, politicians felt that European grain production was outstripping demand, and as mentioned in the previous chapter, this led to the Community's Common Agricultural Policy. For European farmers such political decisions

The abiding memory of stooking sheaves is of prickles from thistles in the crop. Modern sprays mean no weeds are visible as this New Holland TX63 devours this crop of barley in the Gloucestershire Cotswolds.

had a big impact. By setting the rates of various allowances or payments, politicians can make a crop profitable or unprofitable. Politicians will claim that their options are constrained by international agreements like the General Agreement on Tariffs and Trade. Meanwhile, growers in the Soviet Union blamed centralised bureaucracy, and even in the United States schemes were introduced to restrict output.

Each country's negotiating position is determined by the effect of pressure and campaigning by its farmers and consumers. Plenty of lip-service is paid to the needs of the starving millions, but an impartial observer would accept that they usually come off less well from such deals. As an interesting aside, see if you can guess the answer to the following question. At the end of the 20th century roughly 278 million tonnes of grain was in store and judged surplus to immediate requirements. If there was a worldwide catastrophe and harvests totally failed, how long

would this last at our present rate of consumption? The surprising answer is at the end of the chapter.

Individual farmers had no direct influence on these factors. However, they could work out how to make the best of any scheme on their farm. With set-aside, for example, some made sure that it was their lowest yielding land that was left uncultivated.

In Britain only 59,000 farmers remained eligible for Arable Aid payments. Many of the farms no longer eligible successfully grew cereals when Britain faced shortages during World War 2.

All these changes reduced demand for new combines, so it is no wonder that salesmen found it such a challenge to sell new machines. To make matters worse, it was often the high cost of replacing a combine that made a farmer stop and take a close financial look at the future of his business.

However, another group of politicians was opening up new markets for combine makers. As democracy returned to the Soviet Union, many newly independent nations emerged. Formerly their state farms system had relied on Soviet-built combines, which often suffered from unreliability and delays in getting spares. While farm managers and planners were keen to get more reliable combines, they had no capital to buy them. Only aid packages and special

This Clayson 8050 is awaiting a new owner at a farm disposal sale. The vendor had decided that cereal growing is unprofitable and in future a neighbour would contract farm his land. Falling returns from cereal growing have made many farmers decide that owning a combine is an unnecessary luxury.

financial terms made it possible to consider Western alternatives.

In Britain the 'Assured Combinable Crops Scheme' was introduced, which claimed to set minimum standards in relation to record-keeping, maintenance of equipment, crop nutrition, environmental best practice, crop protection, and storage and transportation. Farmers were assured that signing up to it 'will offer purchasers and consumers genuine assurance about the production, handling and storage of combinable crops on farms'. To independent-minded farmers this represented yet another distraction involving what in their opinion were relatively minor points. Few farmers enjoy record-keeping — they would much sooner be out of the office making something happen. The thought of inspections made a few more farmers wonder whether it was worth continuing to grow cereals.

Right: Combine World is a combination of dealers marketing second-hand combines traded in against new ones. The majority of combines are resold within Britain, but overseas buyers appreciate the choice available from a single source.

Below: This Claas Mega 218 has had all its lights removed in preparation for dispatch by rail to a buyer in Russia, where imported combines are supplementing locally made machines. Both new and used machines are finding plenty of work waiting for them.

Far left: The combination of regulations and accepted good practice has meant that British farmers operate to high standards. To demonstrate this, many farmers have accepted external monitoring of their quality control procedures. This logo was awarded to farms that met the standards.

Left: Among 'combinable crops', field beans are not popular with combine drivers. Wet green material can build up inside the machine, and even worse, as it is often the last crop of the year, extensive cleaning is needed before a machine is fit to store. Neglect of cleaning can lead to corrosion over the winter.

Middle left: In the British climate some crops rarely ripen enough for a combine. Forage maize makes excellent winter feed for dairy cattle, and both stalk and grain are chopped by this New Holland FX450 forage harvester. Considerable power is needed to get the throw seen here. In a drier climate maize would ripen enough for harvesting with a combine fitted with a similar header.

Bottom left: Maize stems are too stout to be cut with an ordinary cutter bar, so specialised headers like this Kemper are needed to cut and present the crop. Since forage maize does not need to ripen, varieties can be grown that continue to add bulk when cereal crops have stopped growing and are ripening. As a result, in terms of cattle feed the maize crop will out-yield a cereal grain crop, although, as ruminants, only cattle can make full use of its feed value.

Below: A Claas Classic 98 at work direct-cutting peas in the late evening. When ripe enough for combining, peas form an awkward tangled mass, and ideally the driver wants them to be leaning towards the cutter bar, which may mean cutting in one direction only. Correctly set, the reel pulls the crop up and over the cutter bar. Peas harvested this way are far too ripe for freezing, and most go as animal feed, although the best samples may go for 'mushy' or processed peas.

Bottom: A closer view of the combine header. The polished silver divider is the first part to meet the crop. The large red drum is the rotating reel, and, set low, it urges the crop back on to the cutter bar. Correct positioning of the reel can increase the speed at which the combine will cut the crop; it is raised and lowered by one hydraulic ram, while a second moves the reel backwards and forwards.

Left: A Massey Ferguson 6170 tractor and Welger AP730 conventional baler make a start at clearing straw behind a combine. There is still a demand for smaller bales, and some buyers will now pay a premium for the convenience of being able to manhandle individual bales.

Below left: Clearing up straw with a John Deere 550 round baler. The threshed straw is picked up in a continuous mat and rolled by the rubber belts, then several turns of string hold the bale secure before it is discharged as here. An even swathe helps to produce such uniform firm bales.

Right: When first made, round bales are awkward to stack and their dimensions make it difficult to get a full load on to a lorry. By contrast, 2.5m high-density big bales fit the width of a lorry and can be stacked to make a dense and stable load. Not surprisingly they are popular with merchants who have to transport large quantities of straw.

Below: Once round bales are stacked they gradually settle to form a solid stack. Even without weather protection the bales shed much of the rain, and even when discoloured with damp the lower layers will still be dry and usable. Never be tempted to climb a stack like this — people have been killed or badly injured by a falling round bale.

Meanwhile, combine design was becoming fairly well established and most of the trends were visible. International had one surprise, however. Their Axial Flow combines had the drum (known as the rotor) mounted lengthways internally. With the straw fed in from one end, it could make two or three revolutions before it emerged from the rear of the drum. This gave a far bigger drum and concave for the grain to pass through, and also gave the design a huge appetite for work. In turn, this inspired other makers to consider some form of rotary design; New Holland, for example, went for twin rotors.

This background helps to explain the odd mixture of combines to be seen at work in fields. Some are big, modern machines fitted with comfortable cabs, while others can be seen with no cab and carrying very old registration marks. Are you looking at a backward farmer or just a shrewd one? Typically, old combines are run by a farmer who is unwilling to tie up a lot of money in a large and expensive machine that will be of limited use on his farm. He would appreciate being out of the dust, heat and noise of an open combine seat, but will not always be willing to pay the heavy extra cost of that comfort. While some people feel that they need a first-class hotel, others take a tent.

Left: On an Axial Flow combine the threshing drum is mounted lengthways. Introduced by International Harvester, Axial Flow enables a bigger and wider drum to be used. Despite its compact lines, under the right conditions this design has a high throughput.

Below left: New Holland's answer to the Axial Flow combine was its twin rotor range. This TX34 is being operated by agricultural contractors in south Wiltshire.

Above: The rear-mounted straw chopper has been moved forward out of work, and in this position straw can be discharged on to the stubble behind the combine. The lighter material in front of the chopper consists of short straws, husks and other light material, blown off the sieves. The hitch to tow the header transport can be seen just behind the rear steering axle.

Below: A John Deere 975 at work in the Cotswolds. Even this small amount of dust will make the driver appreciate his cab and the care taken to enclose the engine. Notice how the air cleaner intake for the engine is mounted high up out of the dust.

Little money is spent on genuine spare parts and having them fitted by trained technicians. However, this may not be as much of a problem as it might appear. Over the years farmers have learned the foibles of their machines and can anticipate many breakdowns. It is also quite likely that a similar disused machine is held in reserve as a source of parts. Belts, bearings and engine parts can be sourced from local factors rather than as genuine spare parts, while specialised combine breakers can supply or recondition other parts.

Such a farmer may be late starting combining and early finishing. This is not laziness — there may be other chores to be done. The bonus is that his grain will need less drying. His well-equipped neighbours may sneer at his old-fashioned equipment, and machinery salesmen will urge him to get up to date. They don't spend too long talking, though. They realise that they stand a better chance of selling a new combine to a farmer with a good second-hand machine to trade in.

This farmer has the last laugh on his neighbours, though. Each year their expensive combines will lose thousands of pounds in value. Their grain handling set-up has to cope with the high output from the new and bigger combine. The weight of the bigger combine leaves ruts in wet years that need more cultivation. Even those neighbours that use contractors are faced with hefty bills for their services. While his equipment may be old-fashioned, his accounts will show that he is probably getting his grain harvested far more cheaply than his 'progressive' neighbours.

What you are probably looking at is a farmer with a talent for keeping old machinery running. No doubt he still enjoys being a farmer despite the aggravations. He is likely to be handy with tools and a practical engineer. Machinery salesmen fret that other, more progressive farmers will seek to extend the working life of their equipment in the future. To add to the confusion, some collectors now enjoy rescuing and restoring old combines and demonstrating them at work.

As mentioned several times before, a new combine harvester is an expensive and sophisticated machine to buy, and needs a skilful driver to get the best from it. As a result we have returned to the situation we saw in the early days of combines: not every machine you see is owned by the farmer on whose land it is working. While large and progressive farmers might buy a combine outright, others prefer to pay a contractor to bring in a machine and use it. Often the contractor might be another farmer or his son seeking extra work for his own machinery.

Fewer combines are each harvesting a bigger area each year. Often a new combine is justified as doing the work previously done by two. As combines get bigger, fewer farmers have two combines to replace. This is a worry for manufacturers. Who will buy their machines? In the 1980s accountants at the big manufacturers made an uncomfortable discovery. If farmers are losing money they will not buy shiny new machinery, and low grain prices led to cereal farmers taking outside employment to offset losses.

Waste not, want not: if you deal in combines how do you deter unwelcome visitors when you are closed? One dealer has topped his gates with old combine knives — simple but effective!

Above: Hiring out combines was pioneered by the Agricultural Plant Hire Group. Here a modern New Holland is contrasted with a Claas Self Propelled at the Royal Show. In the adjoining marquee professional advisers are presenting their thoughts on 'The Cost of a Combine', the hope being that the audience will consist of people willing to pay.

Below: Another answer is for landowners to have their land farmed on contract, and such specialist contractors can make effective use of big machines, which need plenty of work each year to keep the cost per acre acceptable. Here a Lexion 460 is making short work of a field of oil-seed rape in Gloucestershire.

A wider header means that combine discharge spouts need to be longer, since, when collecting grain on the move, the front of the tractor has to be able to run alongside the header, putting the trailer in the right position for the grain to fall into it. Here the trailer is being filled with the combine stationary — the AS trailer is relatively small for such a heavy discharge, so this is a sensible decision by the team.

As sales fell the question was reversed. Who would buy the manufacturer? This trend started when Fiat bought Laverda in 1975. In 1984 it added French builder Braud, which, as well as building combines, had an international reputation for grape harvesters. By 1985 both Case and International had been reporting declining sales and profits for the previous five years. In a surprise move Case bought 'selected parts' of International, which resulted in Case-IH. Case had gone from building steam engines and separators to trailed combines, but was better known in the United States; many remember the imported wartime Case LA, a powerful but thirsty tractor to drive a threshing drum. The Case name returned to Britain when Tenneco (Case's parent company) used it following the take-over of David Brown Tractors.

In 1986 Ford Tractor took over Sperry New Holland to form Ford New Holland. This added combines to the range that Ford could persuade its dealers to sell, but within a few years Ford decided that it was really a car company and sold off its tractor and combine business to Fiat. This brought Laverda, Braud and New Holland under the same ownership. To the surprise of many people Fiat

decided to extend the New Holland name to former Ford tractors.

In the mid-1990s big orders started flowing from the former Soviet republics for more modern equipment. Case IH, for example, sold around 700 Axial Flow combines to the big cereal-growing areas of Turkmenistan and Uzbekistan. As part of the deal they had to supply back-up and training as well as buying into a factory making cotton pickers in Tashkent. A pattern emerged whereby each republic tended to buy one particular make in large quantities: Bashkortostan, for example, ordered 200 New Holland TX combines.

In Poland New Holland took over the Bizon combine works, and in 1997 Case acquired Fortschritt, based in former East Germany. Just before, Fortschritt had been reported to be working on a modified layout of combine, feeling that it was time steering was done through the front axle.

When Fiat bought Case IH the two former rivals found themselves under common ownership in a business that became known as Case New Holland (CNH). As part of the take-over the Doncaster tractor factory had to be sold, but the new owner, Landini, has revived the McCormick name for tractors.

One of the original pioneers of combine harvesters, the Caterpillar Company, decided to return to the combine business, and in an arrangement with Claas, Lexion combines are sold as Caterpillars in the US fitted with Caterpillar engines. In a reminder of the early days, the company offered the option of Caterpillar rubber tracks to reduce sinkage by wheels, this time on heavy combines. Shortly Lexions will be built in the USA at a new plant under construction. In the past, other makers have offered tracks for combines working in rice. Some users hope that rubber tracks might reduce the ground compaction caused by a heavily laden combine but still let it travel on highways.

These events were much more than just a merger of combine makes. There were similar overlaps in earth-moving equipment and tractors. John Deere, meanwhile, has been rather more restrained, and has just got on with consolidating and growing its business.

A specially formed company called Varity bought Massey Ferguson, but after a few years, disappointing sales persuaded it to sell the company on again. This time it was bought by AGCO, a firm established in 1990. There is a curious link with combines here, as the trading name is derived from the Allis Gleaner Company, which had previously been selling Deutz tractors in the US. Varity later sold Perkins Engines to Caterpillar. AGCO revived the Gleaner name to run alongside White Combines, while also buying in combines made by Dronningborg in Denmark to sell under the Massey Ferguson name. AGCO then bought Fendt, the German tractor manufacturer, and started to apply the Fendt name on Dronningborg combines for some markets.

A startling reminder of just how far we have travelled from the man with the scythe. A Claas Lexion 480 like this set a harvesting record by gathering over 40 tonnes of grain in an hour, while the Claas Self Propelled was reckoned to be a high-output machine with a potential work rate of just 4 tonnes per hour. For our man with a scythe, harvesting and threshing even 1 tonne of grain with a flail would have taken the equivalent of a week! *J. Mann*

The smallest of the Claas Lexion range is the 410, seen here waiting to parade at the Three Counties Show. Small is, of course, only a relative term in this range.

Right: The shape of the future: three of the six Claas Lexions working in former East Germany on a large farm. Their cutting width is 9 metres (30 feet), and sophisticated electronics are fitted to plot yields against location. The Claas Caterpillar Challenger tractor on the right is fitted with rubber tracks to reduce ground pressure and increase traction. With its chaser trailer, its job is to transfer grain from the combines to waiting lorries for transport back to the farm store. Under a recently established agreement Caterpillar are marketing Claas combines in the United States, while Claas are offering Caterpillar agricultural equipment in Europe. Production of Lexion combines is planned to start soon in the US and these will feature Caterpillar engines for even greater power and the option of rubber tracks for reduced ground pressure. *J. Mann*

This page: Fitting the header is now a quick job with a Claas. On the elevator are two lugs on hydraulic rams, which plug into two brackets on the header. As the elevator is lifted the header hangs on the two lugs, and the weight of the header causes the bottoms to swing together. A downward tug on the lever and the large-diameter pins are inserted into matching holes on the elevator, firmly locking the two parts together. Connecting the guarded power shaft and hydraulic services completes the job. With a suitable transport trailer, coupling and uncoupling can be a very quick job.

Right: Designers continue to provide safer access to combines. On this John Deere 1174, the combination of ladder, steps and guard rails makes access to the high-mounted engine easy for servicing and inspection. Also the rear lights can be folded in as shown when not needed on the road.

Transporting combines on roads is an important consideration as the machines become ever larger. After this New Holland TX63 has polished off its job, the problem arises of getting such a wide machine to its next field. The width can be reduced by detaching the header for separate transport. Mechanag of Tisbury, Wiltshire, specialise in header transport trailers. The adjustable clamps are set up to receive the header safely and hold it firmly in the right attitude for easy recoupling. Once loaded it can be towed either behind the combine or by an escorting tractor.

Here the header from a modern Massey Ferguson is carried on a simple trailer. With the header removed, the main machine can easily travel by road. With two amber beacons, four headlights and four more work lights mounted in top of the cab, it will not easily be missed! Combines sold as Massey Ferguson are now built by Dronningborg in Denmark. Note to the driver's right the Daniavision computer screen on which are presented information and warnings.

When on the road, meeting a tractor pulling a trailer transporting a combine header is a possible warning of the main machine ahead. In this case a John Deere is on the move to its next job. With the header removed, the combine can travel without the need of a special escort. Even so, a speeding motorist might be faced with a narrow gap to squeeze through. Once in the next field the header can be refitted and work can commence. With a chopper hard at work the straw literally disappears, leaving almost no residue to trouble the ploughman.

Right: A good demonstration of something that can confuse satellite tracking systems. The Axial Flow combine approaching is not taking a full-width cut; if the computer assumes it is, the suggested yield will be disappointing.

All the big combine makers are now much more firmly associated with a full line of equipment. Since all makes are capable of doing an acceptable job, the manufacturers' aim has been to try and persuade a farmer to buy as much of his machinery needs as possible from the same source. There has been one curious consequence: in some cases combine owners have been associated with a particular make longer than the people that actually form the top management or shareholders.

The most significant changes in combine design recently have been well concealed. Far more information is being gathered during harvest, and this is done using satellite technology. Remarkable TV news reports during the Gulf War showed how missiles could be targeted at a specific address, representing a huge improvement in accuracy compared with earlier methods of bomb-aiming. Electronics on board each missile constantly calculated the exact position of several US military satellites, enabling it to plot the exact location of the missile at any moment. Small changes in position were enough to work out the exact speed and height of the missile in flight. Since the missile had the same information for its destination, it was relatively easy to adjust the controls to fly towards the intended target.

This technology is now being used on combines — electronics constantly work out its exact position. A cynic might think that looking out of the cab window would be sufficient. However, the intention is to calculate and record the exact route taken by the combine. Now add an attachment that can weigh the amount of grain harvested during a short period. Done frequently enough, the driver can learn the spot rate of harvesting in tonnes per hour, rather like a speedometer. A running total reveals the tonnage harvested from a given area or during a given period. Some correction might be needed to allow for any reduction in weight caused by drying the grain before it is fit to sell, and the yield-recording apparatus will need to be recalibrated to allow for the different characteristics of, say, wheat and oil-seed rape.

You might think that all this information is very interesting but of little real use. However, once the various instruments can be made to 'talk' to each other, the situation changes. Put all this information together and a map can be plotted showing the amount of grain harvested from different parts of the field. Modern electronics can do this at the press of a button without involving the driver at all. Such maps usually reveal variations within the field, and users hope that variations in fertilizer and spray treatment can encourage all parts of the field to yield as well as the best bits.

To a modern farm manager this can be very impressive. Similar positioning equipment can be fitted to fertilizer spreaders and sprayers so that the treatment across the field can be varied automatically. At its simplest this can be done manually, but settings can be predetermined automatically according to the yields plotted.

Most manufacturers have built up a system that works on these lines, and this is where the big mergers are leading. A combine will supply data that

Plot trials are used to assess the potential of new varieties and the value of spray treatments, and small combines are still needed for these. In 2000 this Claas Compact 25 was on the move to its next job; in effect, its operators would be hoping to use it to predict the future of farming in five or ten years.

Where grain is to be used for seed it needs to be dressed (graded) to a particularly high standard. Contractors operate a mobile seed dressing service to prepare grain on the farm for use as seed. With the equipment stationary, they can achieve a far higher standard than is possible with a combine harvester.

can be fed to other equipment of the same make, and a farmer will be invited to purchase an integrated line of machinery from a single supplier. While they are all painted the same colour, machines can be sourced from plants in different continents, but as far as the user is concerned they form one unified range.

Investors, clients and managers are particularly impressed. Maps of high and low yielding spots within a field give them the illusion that they can influence how future crops will grow. However, sceptical voices can still be heard. Even the most old-fashioned farm worker will claim to be able to explain most of the causes of variations shown from his knowledge of the field and its history. Typically a low-yielding area might be the site of a former runway or even a demolished building. A south-facing slope will get more sun than a west-facing one. Poor drainage in a low spot might mean that the crop got a bad start over the winter. Erosion could mean shallow soil at the top of a hill with the surplus washed down to make better soil at the bottom.

None the less, with possible errors smoothed by

sophisticated averaging techniques, users hope to rely on these maps to determine future fertilizer and spray treatment. They hope it will reduce costs and increase output. Typically potential savings are claimed to be about 5-10 per cent against one uniform application over the whole field, although the savings would be rather less if the operator applying the uniform rate had been allowed to use his common sense to adjust application rates.

One early user found that the most effective use of these maps was to identify the least productive areas of fields to put them into set-aside.

No doubt these systems will be particularly useful to businesses where the managers frequently change. In many ways studying these maps will go some way to replace the knowledge that more traditional farmers used to acquire by walking over and examining their land.

With satellite navigation widely accepted on sophisticated combines, it can only be a matter of time before tracking is used to establish the most efficient way to cut the field. Soon it could guide the combine without the intervention of the driver. Already Claas offers a laser guidance system, which relies on and measures the difference in signals bouncing back from a cut and a standing crop. This generates a signal that permits precise steering without the operator touching the steering wheel. However, he still sits in the cab, so no unmanned combines yet!

All these sophisticated electronics are being built into combines with four main intentions. First, it is assumed that the more information that is recorded, the more effectively the farm will be managed. Second, armed with this information the farm manager will be able to make decisions more rapidly and more easily, so will be able to farm or manage a larger area of land. Third, it is claimed that the instrumentation will make the driver's job easier and more pleasant. Fourth, it will persuade users to replace their existing combine(s).

As machines get bigger and more efficient, fewer people will be needed to take on the awesome task of keeping the world fed. To give you some idea of the work to be done by combines worldwide, visit the International Grain Council website at www.igc.org.uk. This is an intergovernmental organisation charged with monitoring international grain trade and administering the Grains Trade Convention 1995. Its published estimates of grain production in the last year of the 20th century were 1,469 million tonnes, yet the world consumed it all plus 8 million tonnes drawn from the reserves of 278 million tonnes. This means that there is still plenty of work ahead for combines around the world, but it does leave one worrying thought.

Entering the new millennium with a grain reserve amounting to 278 million tonnes sounds pretty impressive, but it would last the world about two months! Next time you see a combine at work, just bear in mind how urgently the world needs the grain it is harvesting. If combines stop, we starve. If the crop to be harvested fails, the combines have nothing to harvest.

Only two months later the IGC forecast of production had fallen by 17 million tonnes and world stocks by 33 million tonnes, while estimated consumption had risen by 9 million tonnes. Bear in mind that these estimates are what the world is actually going to eat. They are not what the starving would like to eat. Only then do you realise just how vital it is that those combines keep working.

As a result, a wide variety of combines differing in size and age currently harvest crops. They range from those on smaller farms, which are still running machines 30 or 40 years old and do the job eventually, through bigger farms whose careful maintenance is keeping 20-year-old machines working, to contractors and contract farming companies that find it makes good sense to operate modern high-output machines, which, provided there is a big enough area to be harvested, can be economical.

Operators now enjoy all levels of comfort, ranging from unashamed pampered luxury in an air-conditioned cab with a high-quality sound system, to the hardy type to whom luxury is extra padding on the seat. But whatever machine they are driving, and wherever you see them harvesting, they are doing a vital job.

On a bright day the tinting of the cab glass reduces the load on the air-conditioning. High-output Case-IH Axial Flow 1660 machine keeps up the good work.

Above: A Claas Dominator 88 at work in Wiltshire in near-ideal conditions. The crop is clean and upstanding, the weather is warm and dry, the cab is cool, comfortable and dust-free, and the driver's favourite tape is playing. For a few hours this is about as good as combining can get.

Below: How most of us see combines at work: in a cloud of dust this Claas has just finished discharging another load of grain and is pushing on with the harvest while the trailer returns to the grain store.